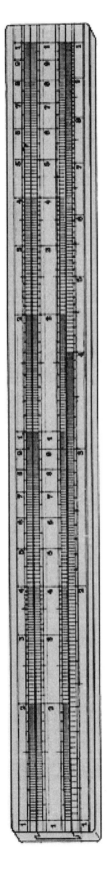

Slide Rules

A Journey Through
Three Centuries

by Dieter von Jezierski

Translated from the German by Rodger Shepherd, M.D., M.P.H

Astragal Press
Mendham, New Jersey

The first edition of this book was published by the author in 1997 under the title

Rechenschieber – eine Dokumentation
Geschichte   Hersteller   Modelle

This translated second edition is published by

The Astragal Press
5 Cold Hill Road, Suite 12
P.O. Box 239
Mendham, NJ 07945-0239

ISBN 1-879335-94-8
Library of Congress Card Number: 00-107501

Cover design by Donald Kahn

PREFACE

I served as product manager at A.W. Faber-Castell through the end of the slide rule era and remained on to manage the Faber-Castell line of drafting instruments, but my interest in slide rules continued. In recent years an accumulation of inquiries from former slide rule users and from slide rule collectors convinced me of the need to fill an information gap. This book was made possible by collecting slide rule literature, relevant catalogs, information from former slide rule craftsmen, as well as my own experiences during some 20 years in contact with slide rule makers and experts.

The book is not a guide to using the slide rule! It is directed at slide rule aficionados, and the goal is to assemble, from various sources, facts worth knowing about slide rules. The book is written from one German's point of view; it reflects my interests (which many collectors in the United States and the United Kingdom may well share). For example, I do not deal fully with the many English slide rules made before the end of the 1800's, or with circular rules. Clearly these, and other highly interesting models, could merit books themselves.

Also this book could not be free of "gaps" because the end of the slide rule era was so sudden and disruptive that complete collections of models and catalogs were not preserved. I feel it is important that knowledge about these subjects be preserved, and books like this one can make their contributions to such preservation. Perhaps my book will stimulate more eyewitnesses to the slide rule era to offer assistance with subsequent editions.

I beg the reader's understanding when, on some pages, I list many slide rule models. I do this in order to help slide rule collectors understand the variety of rules that were offered and can be collected.

I was pleased by the warm reception that the German edition of my book received, and I have been encouraged to make the book accessible to the large number of slide rule collectors in the United States and other English-speaking countries and to other scholars who are interested in the history of technology.

Also, I must acknowledge the need to make some changes. First of all, I felt the need to expand the text for the new readers so that they would have the opportunity to learn more about the development of the slide rule in their own country – especially about those who contributed to the development of the slide rule and those who were the significant makers of slide rules.

Second, as was gently pointed out by Professor Joachim Fischer, some experts, and collector friends, the German edition did not provide enough citations. In this English edition I have taken great pains to provide citations wherever possible. In the process I have gained new respect for the scholars who do this task well.

Third, readers of the German edition have called my attention to other opportunities to make important corrections and additions. All these suggestions were taken into consideration in the preparation of this new, expanded, English edition. My hope is that this book will provide stimulating and satisfying reading for all who open its covers.

I close with a sentence from Ovid, which the distinguished Italian slide rule pioneer Professor Quintinius Sella offered as preface to his slide rule text book in 1859:

"Da veniam scriptis, quorum non gloria nobis causa, sed utilitas officiumque fuit".

["Be lenient about my book, for I did not write it to seek personal fame. I wrote it out of a feeling of responsibility and because I wanted to be useful to someone."]

Dieter von Jezierski
July 2000
Stein, Germany

ACKNOWLEDGEMENTS

I wish to express my gratitude for the encouragement and assistance that I received in preparing both the German and English versions of this book.

I began my research for the German edition of this book in 1991. Fortunately, about that time, the Oughtred Society began publishing its *Journal*, which provided very high quality source material. More recently other useful publications have appeared. Of course I also benefited from the exchange of information with other slide rule collectors.

The following individuals made particularly important contributions to the German edition: Günter Kugel, Dr.-Ing. E.h., provided helpful research as well as expert advice that was always motivating. Hans Dennert, Dipl. Ing., the last proprietor of the Aristo-Werke, Hamburg, graciously authorized the use of pictures from the Aristo Jubilee Report of 1962. Thomas Münstermann, Dipl. Ing., arranged crucial preparations for the printing of the book. Professor Gunter Erhard, Dr.-Ing., Harold Riehle, Dipl. Ing., principal at IWA, F. Riehle GMBH&Co., and Heinz Joss, Dipl.Arch, ETH, SIA, were also very helpful with the German edition. Heinz Joss also contributed valuable information about Daemen-Schmid to the English edition.

Rodger Shepherd, M.D., M.P.H., deserves my special thanks for his expert and dedicated translation of the German edition of my book. In addition he also provided advice and assistance about how to make this English version better suited to the American reader.

Finally, I am deeply grateful to Martyl Pollak and the Astragal Press for undertaking the publication of the English version of my book.

This book is dedicated to my grandson Christian.

DvJ

TABLE OF CONTENTS

TABLE OF ILLUSTRATIONS

INTRODUCTION

Buildings, bridges, machines, cars, airplanes, roads, indeed most of the achievements of modern times, were worked out and built with the help of the slide rule. The slide rule was the constant companion and professional tool of innumerable humans. Yet seldom has an object with such an unprecedented history of triumphs, and beloved by millions of people, also experienced such a sudden demise as the slide rule did in 1974.

When Edmund Gunter conceived of the logarithmic scales in 1620, and thereby laid the groundwork for the slide rule, he could not have had any idea what immense significance his invention would have for human progress. First the English, then the French, Americans, Germans, Japanese, and many others, participated decisively in the ongoing development of the slide rule. The number of slide rule users is difficult to estimate, but it must have been many million.

In the age of the computer, the electronic calculator, and magnificent technical advances, this book should provide a hint of what, for all who knew and used the slide rule, is a very nostalgic memory.

The slide rule has earned the right to have its history, the names of its makers, and the kinds and variety of its models preserved for the future.

The History of Slide Rules

Gunter and the English Origins of the Slide Rule

The Englishman Edmund Gunter (1581-1626), with his brilliant idea of transforming logarithms into distances along a straight edge, laid the crucial foundation for the development of the slide rule. Around 1620 he introduced his famous Gunter scale – the forerunner of later slide rules. At that time he was Professor of Astronomy at Gresham College (near London), a recognized center of scientific activity.

However, first we should mention two other Englishmen who put forward the concepts on which Gunter's pioneering invention was based. These Englishmen were Gunter's two contemporaries, John Napier (1550-1617) and Henry Briggs (1561-1630).

Lord John Napier, Baron of Merchiston, was a Scottish landowner with numerous interests. He occupied himself with problems of agriculture. For example, he worked on the improvement of fertilizer and also on the problem of removing water from coal mines. He devoted himself intensively to religious questions. However, his greatest passion was mathematics. [1]

Fig.1. John Napier
1550-1617

In 1614 Napier published his book *Mirifici logarithmorum Canonis Descriptio*, in which he described "the wonderful rule of logarithms." The book included a table of logarithms that made it possible to reduce multiplication and division to addition and subtraction. He had worked almost twenty years on this publication.

It is interesting that Napier, with the publication of his paper in 1614, stole the march on the Swiss instrument maker and astronomer Jost Bürgi (1552-1632). Bürgi had already prepared tables of logarithms during 1603-1611; however he did not decide to submit and publish his work until 1620. [2]

Even if logarithms like Napier's had not been published when they were, a corresponding advance would have come about eventually as the result of the work of Henry Briggs, the Professor of Geometry at Gresham. It was he who recognized the advantages of logarithms to the base 10 (also known as the Briggsian logarithms). One of Napier's admirers, Briggs taught his students about Napier's logarithms, and Briggs visited Napier in 1615 and 1616. By the time of the second visit, Briggs may have shown Napier the tables that he had already developed using the base 10. [3]

Briggs' publication of the first thousand 8-place logarithms (to the base 10) in *Logarithmorum chilias prima*, published in 1617 shortly after Napier's death, was followed by publication of 14-place logarithms for the numbers from 1-20,000 and 90,000-100,000. (These 14-place tables were completed in 1628 by the Dutchman Adrian Vlacq.) Next came Briggs' publication of the logarithms for the trigonometric functions sine, tangent, and secant. [4]

Now, let us return to the activities of Edmund Gunter.

We know that Gunter was born in Hertfordshire, not far from London, and was educated at the Westminster School. Like many other scholars of his time, he accepted a post as pastor, his first post being in the St. George's parish of Southwork.

In 1603 he published (in Latin) *New Projection on the Sphere*. This publication brought him in contact with Henry Briggs and William Oughtred for the first time. At that time Oughtred was already a widely recognized professor of mathematics at Gresham School and was yet to play his important role in the later transformation of Gunter's rule into the slide rule.

In 1618 Gunter introduced his "quadrant." This was a device for determining the hours of the day and the azimuth. The quadrant also was useful for other astronomical and geometric purposes. A year later he became Professor of Astronomy at Gresham College and in the following year his friendship with his colleague Henry Briggs led to his work *Canon Triangulorum or Table of Artificial Sinus or Tangents, to a radius of 100,000 parts to each minute of the Quadrant*. Thus Gunter created a table of logarithms for sine and tangent, just as Briggs had done for the natural numbers. In this connection Oughtred later wrote, "The honour of the invention of the Logarithms, next to Lord of Merchiston, and our Mr. Briggs belongthed to Master Gunter, who exposed their numbers upon a straight line. And what does the new instrument (of mine) called the circle of proportion but only bow and reflect Master Gunter's line or rule." [5]

With that Oughtred confirmed Gunter's role in the development of logarithms and their transformation into lineal distances on the Gunter rule, from which Oughtred's own circular rule later was derived.

Gunter coined the terms cosine and cotangent, developed an apparatus for surveying (the "Gunter chain"), and wrote many publications on astronomy and geometry. However, his greatest invention (and the one that remained in use the longest) was the Gunter rule, which he reported in *Canon Triangulorum...* and later (1623) in *Description and Use of the Sector, Cross Staff, and other Instruments*. [6] With the Gunter rule, he had brilliantly converted logarithmic values into graphic form over a distance of 24 inches. This became the basis for all subsequent slide rules and their scales.

The year of his invention can be considered either 1620, the year that *Canon Triangulorum...* was published in England, or 1624, when he reported his invention to the Paris Academy of Science.

The so-called Gunter scale was a straightedge made of boxwood, and the original was about 60 cm (2 feet) long and about 5 cm (2 inches) wide. It was beveled on one edge. Logarithmic and decimal scales were laid out on the front and back sides. In subsequent years the Gunter scale, i.e., the arrangement of scales originally developed by him, experienced many changes. As a result, it is difficult now to determine the demarcation between variants.

The extensive literature regarding the historical development of the slide rule does not treat the Gunter rule with the requisite clarity. This is especially true of the literature around the turn of the 19th century. Consequently, misunderstandings arose over and over again as a result of the use of the term "Gunter scale." This term was often applied to the whole rule, but the term could mean only the logarithmically divided scale from 1 to 100. Clearer indeed was the designation "Gunter scale" for his boxwood straightedge (which mariners called the "Gunter") and the designation "Gunter line" or "line of proportion" for the corresponding "A scale" from 1 to 100.

The oldest known Gunter scale is described by Albert Rohrberg [7] and is also depicted in Dennert & Pape's Jubilee book. [8]

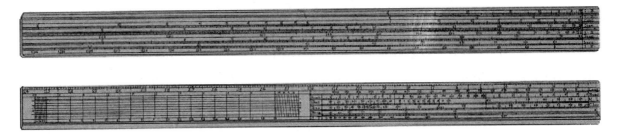

Fig.2. The front and back of the Gunterscale before the modifications by B. Donn

The front side bears the following scales (listed from the top down):

S. R.	(sines of the rhumbs)	= sine of the compass point
T. R.	(tangent of the rhumbs)	= tangent of the compass point
Numb	(Numbers)	= the crucial Gunter line, which corresponded to the subsequent A scale
Sine	(sinus)	= the logarithmic sine scale, referenced to the Numb scale
V.S.	(versed sine)	= the inverted sine line for cos (1/2x)
Tang	(tangents)	= the logarithmic tangent scale
Meri	(meridian line)	= the meridian line
E.P.	(equal parts)	= decimal, retrograde from 0 to 190.

In addition to the Numb line, both the Sine scale (later called the S scale) and the Tang (later called the T scale) became essential elements of the modern technical slide rule.

The rest of the scales on the Gunter rule served for nautical and astronomical calculations made at sea. In England these scales were particularly important, and Edmund Gunter concerned himself repeatedly with these topics.

There is no question that the Gunter scale, with its many enhancements, was used by sea captains (including Admiral Nelson) and ships' pilots even to the end of the 19th century, i.e., to a time when the more modern technical slide rule had established its ascendancy. One reason for this was probably the fact that mariners, who found the nautical scales very useful, also had confidence in pointed course dividers (devices which mariners also used during their daily course reckoning). Mariners were quite familiar with the technique of adding and marking off distances with course dividers.

A thorough description of the Gunter scale, with detailed examples of nautical applications and also examples of the most important numerical calculations, is provided in a book by Captain Ludwig Jerrmann dated 1888 and called *The Gunter Scale: A Complete Explanation of the Gunter Line and Evidence Regarding its Origin Plus Numerous Examples of the Scale's Practical Application*. The book includes an illustration of a later and expanded Gunter scale. This scale is marked, "Navigation Scale Improved by B. Donn." [9]

In contrast to the original Gunter scale described above, the Donn version includes two new scales in the place of the E.P. scale on the front (which Jerrmann called the back):

Num Root   (numbers root)   = square root scale = the modern D scale
Num Cube   (numbers cube)   = the cube root scale = the modern K scale.

These two new scales were originated by Edmund Wingate, not by Donn. On the back (which Jerrmann called the front) of the so-called Donn scale is a scale marked Guns Diamr (gun's diameter). This scale was used with an inch scale below and gave the projectile weight in pounds for a cannon with the indicated bore size.

These changes were so insignificant that they did not justify the sometime designation Donn scale for the whole rule; it was still a Gunter scale.

As can be seen below in Figure 3, Captain Jerrmann had clearly identified, in Table III of his book, the really important "slide-rule-relevant" scales. [10]

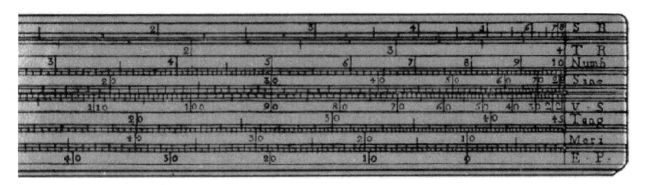

Fig.3. Section of Gunter scale (from the right side of the front)

Of course calculation with the Gunter scale was tedious and complicated. The addition of the distances for $log(a \times b) = log\ a + log\ b$ and the subtraction of the distances for $log(a/b) = log\ a - log\ b$ had to be accomplished with the pointed dividers. For example, in order to multiply 1.97 x 2.56, one placed one point of the divider at the beginning of the Gunter scale and the other at 1.97. This distance was transferred to begin at 2.56 and the result (5.04) was read at the point of the divider to the right. To protect the scales, but also to provide help in positioning the divider point, later models had brass dots imbedded at the beginning of important scales.

If we go back to the beginning of the slide rule, that is to the Gunter scale, we find that Edmund Gunter marked the Numb scale twice on his device. This is discussed by Rolf Jäger, a staff member at Dennert & Pape-Aristo-Werke [11]:

> "I can easily imagine how he carried out testing in his study and how he worked with his dividers to measure off distances and connect them in order to test how accurate the hand marking on the wooden rule had turned out. He began with 2x2 and 2x3. Then came the first disappointment; his scale was not adequate for (for example) 2x6 = 12 because the scale ended at 10. Thus, if he is to avoid changing his divider setting in order to carry the remainder back to 1, then he must diligently make more marks and extend the scale a second

cycle from 10-100. However, if he makes more marks, the scale becomes infinitely long. He probably runs out of space on his strip of wood. Thus he decides to make a new scale next to the D scale (1-10). The new scale is half as big so that he can carry it out to 100. This A scale becomes, in the future, his main scale, with which he can conveniently solve every example of multiplication and division. Finally he drops the D scale completely."

The use of the dividers did not permit rapid calculation, and it was inevitable that Edmund Gunter's transformation of logarithms into distances would attract improvements.

The next logical and decisive development in the evolution of the slide rule was a scale arrangement developed by the Englishmen Oughtred and Wingate, though twentieth century historians argue fiercely about which of these two men gets credit for being first.

However, the main point is that two corresponding scales (1-100, now called the A and B scales) were arranged so that they could move along each other. This was accomplished by equipping two wooden rules with these scales and holding the two rules together in a way that permitted the rules to slide. Oughtred did this.

William Oughtred (1575-1660) was initially a pastor in the Oxfordshire parish. However, he soon occupied himself with mathematics and astronomy, and he became a significant mathematician of his time. In 1618 he wrote the following about his first meeting with Edmund Gunter:

Fig.4. W. Oughtred (1575-1660)

"I being in London, went to see my honoured friend, Master Henry Briggs, who then brought me acquainted with Master Gunter, with whom, falling in speech about his quadrant, I shewed him my horizontall instrument." [12]

Long after this meeting Oughtred transformed the Gunter scale (which had become well known to him) into a spiral and thereby invented the circular slide rule. It was around this time (1627), a year after Gunter's death, that the idea of the sliding logarithmic scales occurred to him.

Oughtred prepared a manuscript in Latin about his innovations. The work appeared in English as *Circle of Proportion, and the Horizontall Instrument* (1632) and *Two rulers of proportion* (1633). [13] His device was made by Elias Allen, a productive instrument maker in London.

For a long time Edmund Wingate (1596-1656), a lawyer who was interested in mathematics, was also credited with the invention of the sliding Gunter scales. In 1624 he went to Paris as the tutor of Princess Henrietta Maria (later Queen of England).

Wingate was in communication with Edmund Gunter and had been introduced to his "rule of proportion" (as Wingate called it). During Wingate's stay in Paris, he introduced the sliding rule into France and made it known to prominent mathematicians.

Wingate published a book called *L'usage de la règle de proportion en arithmetique* (Paris, 1624) which was rushed and incomplete because he wished to be the first to publish. In 1628 the improved English edition appeared as *The Construction and Use of the Line of Proportion, by help whereof the hardest questions of Arithmetique and Geometry, as well in broken as in whole numbers, are resolved by addition and subtraction.*

In any case, Wingate had helped to arrange a breakthrough in France for the Gunter scale or "line of proportion," and a certain William Leybourn [13A] also attributed the "root scales" (square and cube) to Wingate. However, it remains disputed whether he also invented mechanical-logarithmic calculation by means of sliding rules, or whether he simply knew about it. In the end, in a battle of experts, the credit for the first publication was attributed to William Oughtred.

The Great Debate

This battle of experts over who invented the slide rule deserves some discussion.

Florian Cajori (1850-1930) was a central figure in this debate. He was one of the most significant historians of mathematics of his time. In 1875 he emigrated from Switzerland to the U.S. He taught at Tulane University in New Orleans (1885-88) and later at Colorado College (1889-1918). In 1918 he became professor of mathematics at the University of California in Berkeley. He published extensively, but his studies of the history of the slide rule offer an exemplary and incomparable wealth of material. He gets credit for determining and writing about all the important dates, persons, models, and references – beginning with Edmund Gunter's invention through the end of the 19th century.

Fig.5. F. Cajori (1850-1930)

In 1909, when he was teaching at Colorado College, he published his distinguished book, *History of the Logarithmic Slide Rule and Allied Instruments*. This book was reprinted several times, most recently in 1994. On page 14 he says:

> "The conclusions we have reached thus far may be summarized as follows: Edmund Gunter invented a logarithmic line called Gunter's line, but not the slide rule; the straight edge slide rule was first invented by Edmund Wingate and explained by him in several publications, the earliest of which appeared in 1630. Such a slide rule was also given to the world in 1632 by William Oughtred, in a work prepared for the press by William Forster. Oughtred was the first to design a circular slide rule."

This "definitive conclusion," made in favor of Wingate in 1909, was revised in 1920 in Cajori's brochure, *On the History of Gunter's scale and the Slide Rule during the Seventeenth Century*. In the introduction to this brochure Cajori notes:

> "In my history of the slide rule, and my article on its invention it is shewn that William Oughtred and not Edmund Wingate is the inventor…"

Professor E. Hammer (1857-1919) of the Imperial Technical Hochschule of Stuttgart succumbed to the same mistake. (He may have been influenced by Cajori.) Even in the third edition (1904) of Hammer's book *Der Logarithmische Rechenschieber und sein Gebrauch* (The logarithmic slide rule and its use), he names Wingate as the inventor of the sliding scales. However, in the fifth edition (1918) of his book, he, too, corrects himself:

"Of course the present-day slide rule was invented only a few years after the invention of the Gunter scale, when the use of dividers was made dispensable by the arranging for two corresponding Gunter scales to slide along each other.

"This suggestion, which made mechanical-logarithmic calculation with the slide rule so extraordinarily convenient, has, for a long time, been attributed by us and others to the Englishman Edmund Wingate (1596-1660), who contributed much to our knowledge about logarithmic calculation."

As source for this, Hammer cited A. Rohrberg's widely circulated *Theorie und Praxis des logarithmischen Rechenschiebers* ("Theory and Practice of Logarithmic Slide Rules" 1916). Hammer continued as follows:

"However, already in 1842 A. de Morgan [14], who was exceptionally well informed, had declared it probable that William Oughtred, not Wingate, deserved the credit for this invention which made the Gunter scale into the slide rule. Professor Cajori has declared this probability to be a certainty."

Furthermore, E. Hammer correctly proved that, in Cajori's Addenda to his 1909 *History of...* and in his further papers, Cajori corrected himself and ascribed to Oughtred the idea of the sliding scales.

The same conclusion is found in M. Hartmuth's *Vom Abacus zum Rechenschieber* (1942) and in the jubilee publication by Dennert and Pape-Aristo-Werke (1962). Representative of many foreign language textbooks and their history sections are the following notations from R.K. Allen's *Systematic Slide Rule Technique* (1962). In his introduction he notes:

"1624. Edmund Wingate used an evenly divided "log scale" from which to read logarithms of numbers on an adjacent scale, and he introduced the Gunter scale to France."

Allan goes on to say:

"1633. The Reverend William Oughtred, living near London, was probably the first to make use of two similar logarithmically divided scales moving lengthwise in relation to each other. They had to be maintained in contact by hand." [15]

A final thought would be fitting. Edmund Gunter died very early, at the age of 45. With the undoubtedly great practical talent that he had, he would probably have discovered these mechanical solutions himself. It is also plausible that his two surviving colleagues put his ideas into action.

In this context the mathematician Richard Delamaine senior [16] should be mentioned. In his work *Grammelogia* he claims credit for inventing the circular slide rule, which was already credited to Oughtred. [17]

Next Steps in the Development of the Slide Rule in England

The third and decisive step in the development of the definitive slide rule was carried out by two more Englishmen, Bissaker and Partridge.

In 1654 Robert Bissaker constructed a slide rule with movable "tongues" or slides, which moved in a stator. This was the forerunner of the subsequent one-sided slide rule. It bears the mark "Made by Robert Bissaker for T.W., 1654". Made of boxwood, it is 60 cm long and 2.5 cm high, and is rectangular in cross section. The ends of the stator are connected with brass fixtures, which hold the stator and slide together even when the slide is pulled out. This slide rule has 19 scales, which are derived from Gunter's logarithmic scales.

Seth Partridge (1603-1686) is named as the inventor (ca. 1657) of a further model, which was fabricated by the London instrument maker Walter Haynes. Partridge was a land surveyor, but he mainly taught mathematics. He even published a book, *The Description and Use of an Instrument called the Double Scale of Proportion*, which went through several editions. His slide rule was composed of three similar strips of wood, which were held together by brass straps at the two ends. The slide moved in the stator. Partridge's invention was the prototype of the subsequent, very practical, double-sided slide rule.

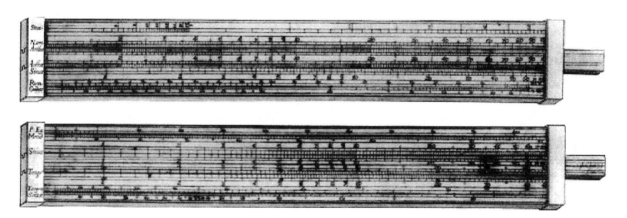

Fig.6. Two-sided slide rule by Seth Partridge

The next decade in England was marked by the development of several more models. These are reported in the catalog of the Science Museum in London and in Cajori's book. (To some extent these slide rules can be organized either by the person who invented and described them or by the maker, including, for example, Carver, J. Fry, Dring & Fage, Troughton, and Nairne & Blunt.)

In England during the second half of the 17th century the slide rule had already established itself. Its advantages – rapid calculation and adequate precision (2-3 places) – were well recognized. Names like Henry Coggeshall and Thomas Everard are associated with the first standard slide rule scale systems, and the slide rules using these scales were produced and used in great numbers.

The new term "sliding rule" was first used by John Brown in a manual that he wrote for a slide rule that he made. In addition to the classic boxwood rules, "sliding rules" were also made of brass and ivory. It was already customary to use brass for nautical rulers, sextants, and dividers. The important applications for slide rules in Everard's time related to navigation, ship building, and the calculation of the volume (e.g., cubic feet) of cargo, casks, and lumber.

Many slide rules were marked with so-called "gauge points" that were used in calculations involving standard measuring units or in the conversion of measuring units. Such slide rules were the first "gaugers" or commercial slide rules.

The next slide rule trend-setter was James Watt (1736-1819), the famous inventor of the steam engine and co-founder of the Bolton & Watt machine factory. [19] He established early criteria and standards for his steam engine, and here the use of the slide rule was a great advantage. At that time slide rules were hand-made, inexact, and – in some cases – unwieldy. Because of this, Watt, with the assistance of one of his colleagues, the mathematician Southern, developed a special slide rule to meet the requirements of his engineers and technicians. Skillful craftsmen at his factory built the first prototypes. Based on these prototypes, the London manufacturer W.S. Jones then produced large numbers of these rules. They were called SOHO slide rules after the place of their development and first application. As the first "technical slide rule," the SOHO rule was widely distributed in England and was a well-known export to the Continent. Two slide rules used by the great James Watt himself are exhibited in the British Museum in a special section devoted to him.

The London Science Museum catalog describes the SOHO rule as follows: "Single-sided slide rule of box wood, approximately 27 cm long, 4 scales on the front: A/B, C/D. Scales A, B, and C run 1-100. Scale D runs 1-10."

The SOHO slide rule is also depicted in the Aristo jubilee issue of 1962, where it is explained that in Watt's time, the A and B scales (1-100) were used for most calculations in order to avoid the shifting involved in using the right index. The jubilee issue goes on to say:

> "The C scale (which in later rules is a sliding scale running 1-10) is still a sliding scale running from 1-100. It is used in connection with the adjacent fixed scale, Scale D, only to determine squares and square roots. When we consider that the SOHO slide rule lacked a cursor, then it is understandable that a one-cycle and a two-cycle scale must be arranged this way." [20]

On the upper and lower edges of the SOHO rule there were scales marked in $1/10$ of an inch and $1/8$ of an inch or in some cases $1/100$ of a foot. In the floor of the stator (area behind the slide), the inch scales continue and permit the use of the slide to measure distances longer than the stator. [21]

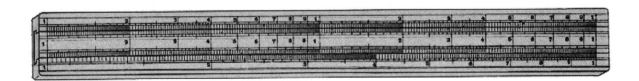

Fig.7. SOHO slide rule by James Watt

Still, the absence of a cursor on the SOHO rule was a big disadvantage, and there was pressure to arrange for as many scales as possible to slide in relationship to each other. This, in turn, led to the construction of slide rules with 2, 3, and 4 slides.

Sir Isaac Newton (1643-1727), the eminent scientist, is also connected with the history of the slide rule and the cursor. In his work on the theory of algebraic equations (1675), he described a method for solving cubic equations. This method involved the use of three logarithmic scales lying one above the other with an overlying vertical hairline, (i.e., a kind of early cursor). [22]

In addition, by around 1775, John Robertson [23], professor of mathematics at the Royal Academy in Portsmouth, had produced a mechanical cursor. Despite his contribution, almost 100 years passed before the cursor became a standard component of the modern slide rule.

In the face of this, slide rule users often improvised by reversing the slide in order to position two scales side by side, even though this resulted in one scale with numbers that were upside down. Around 1797, William Pearson (1767-1847), an astronomer, recommended this procedure for certain calculations, e.g., multiplication, division, squaring numbers, and determining square roots. Variations of this strategy are described in instruction manuals up to the end of the slide rule era.

Also worth mentioning is William Nicholson (1753-1815), who, as editor and publisher of "Nicholson's Journal," devoted himself intensively to the study and further development of slide rules. Through his journal he made calculation with the slide rule more widely known. Among other things, he also concerned himself with achieving higher precision through longer scales (without making the stator longer). The true significance and the application of many of his recommendations were unappreciated during his time, and only first recognized and utilized decades later. [24]

The development of the slide rule during the second half of the 19th century was impaired by various factors. For example, as a result of the conversion of systems of weight and measure after 1824, many special-purpose slide rules, which had previously been heavily used, became unusable. Also, the gauge points that appeared on English slide rules and were used to convert various units of measure were now wrong. In response, new, general-purpose models were developed, although they suffered from the lack of a cursor.

In England, a country oriented toward special purpose slide rules, there were few users of general-purpose slide rules. However, general-purpose slide rules were becoming more significant elsewhere. As French and German manufacturers, recognizing the trend toward general-purpose slide rules, increased their production of such rules toward the end of the 1800's, these foreign models were even included in the offerings of some English manufacturers.

France Carries Development Further

Edmund Wingate had made the Gunter scale known in France by around 1624. As a result of Wingate's influence, French authors started writing about the Gunter scale. One of these French authors was Denis Henrion (died 1640). He was a professor of mathematics and had become distinguished as the author of numerous writings on mathematics. Among other things, he introduced Napierian logarithms into France. In 1630, six years after Wingate's first publication in French, Henrion wrote a discussion of the "èchelle angloise," as he called the Gunter scale.

The French revolution and the era of Napoleon brought better times for the slide rule in France. This was the result of the conversion to the metric system. The required conversion of units, e.g., from inches to centimeters, made the slide rule necessary and thus widely used.

As early as 1821, the Lenoir firm had begun to use machines to mark the scales on slide rules. Lenoir made a boxwood slide rule modeled after the SOHO slide rule of Fa. Jones of London. In its time, the Lenoir slide rule was recognized and respected as the best in the world, and during the first half of the 19th century Lenoir was reputed to be the world's leading producer of slide rules. (The platinum standard meter in Paris bears the mark of the Lenoir firm.) Other slide rule producers of that time included the firms Clouet and Sorgent.

It was the slide rule developed by Amédée Mannheim (1831-1906), however, that was indeed epoch-making. Mannheim eventually became a colonel in the French artillery and professor of geometry at the Ecole Polytechnique in Paris. He became known for outstanding scientific work. By the time he was a student and a lieutenant in the artillery school in Metz, he was already very interested in the slide rule. In 1850 he introduced a new scale system which, after the turn of the century, carried his name throughout the world. His arrangement of scales (A/B and C/D) brought similar scales together, i.e., the 1-100 (two cycle) scales were arranged along the upper interface between the stator and the slide, and the 1-10 (one cycle) scales were arranged along the lower interface.

Fig.8. A. Mannheim (1831-1906)

However, Mannheim's most important contribution was that he picked up the idea of the cursor and developed a version that was fully functional and was used for decades. Recall that, before the Mannheim era, the usual scale arrangement was A/B, B/D where A, B, and B were two-cycle scales (1-100) and D was a one-cycle scale (1-10). W en one used a slide rule with this scale arrangement, squares and square roots could be read across the B/D slide-stator interface. Mannheim's introduction of the cursor made the second B scale unnecessary because the cursor's hairline now made it possible to use the A and D scales to determine squares and square roots.

Mannheim placed sine and tangent scales on the back of the slide. These were arranged so that, when the user turned the slide over, the sine and tangent scales could be used with the A scale.

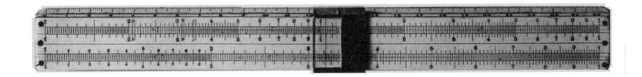

Fig.9. Slide rule of Colonel Mannheim

In 1851 Mannheim reported his ideas in a publication entitled *Règle à calcul modifée*. At this time he also had the good fortune to get the experienced and well-known instrument maker Tavernier-Gravet to make his prototype and produce his slide rule. The Mannheim system was introduced first in France and then gradually in other countries. By the turn of the century the "Mannheim" slide rule had become the standard one-sided model in the American and Japanese markets.

The Mannheim slide rule's fundamental scale arrangement (A/B,C/D) remained the foundation for all further scale systems until the end of the slide rule era. However, Mannheim's greatest contribution was the reintroduction and refinement of a functional cursor. At last, the ideal solution to a long-standing problem!

In the Mannheim system's own country of origin, an interesting variant soon emerged. This was a school version, "la règle des écoles." Along the upper slide-stator interface were two scales which began on the left with square root of 10 (approximately 3.16), continued on through 10(1) and ended on the right with 3.16. Mannheim's one-cycle scales C/D remained along the lower slide-stator interface.

The advantages of this scale arrangement were presented in 1907 by R. Rozè in his textbook *Theorie et usage de la règle à calculs*. One advantage is that the user could avoid switching the slide from right to left in order to use the index at the left. This means that continuous calculations could be done with greater precision. Squares and square roots could be obtained with more precision – although not as easily as with the original Mannheim system.

The "règle des écoles" was widely distributed in France under the name "règle Beghin." A. Beghin was a professor at the industrial school Roubaix and is said to have recommended the scale arrangement seen in "règle des écoles." However, the original idea did not come from Beghin; it came from a Russian, Professor Tscherepaschinski.

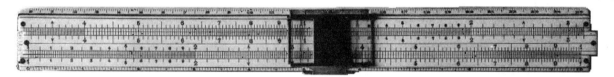

Fig.10. Regle des Ecoles (System Beghin)

In 1882 Tscherepaschinski. sent his design to Tavernier-Gravet for them to make a prototype, and he wrote instructions for the slide rule in Russian. It has not been proven, but it is reasonable to assume that Tavernier-Gravet produced its own version of Tscherepaschinski's slide rule for the French market. Beghin got credit for the introduction of "règle des écoles" because of his instruction book, *Règle a calcul, modèle spécial*, published in 1893 – eleven years after Tscherepaschinski developed this scale arrangement. The book was so successful that, in France, the slide rule described in Beghin's book became identified with his name. Even after the Second World War one French manufacturer, Graphoplex, continued to offer a version of this slide rule (the Rolinea, "derivé du système Beghin"). [25]

With this slide rule developments in France before the turn of the century essentially ended.

United States, Germany, and Japan Climb on Board

In **North America** the slide rule was scarcely known before the beginning of the 19th century. According to Cajori, the use of the slide rule was first described in the United States by Robert Patterson, a professor of mathematics at the University of Pennsylvania, in a book published in 1805. In 1813, in a Baltimore reprint of another English book, a slide rule for carpenters is mentioned. However, for a long time the use of the slide rule, especially by engineers and other technical people, was uncommon.

An important discussion of the slide rule was published in the United States in 1856 by Charles Haslett, a civil engineer, and Charles W. Hackley, a professor of mathematics. This discussion appeared in the *Mechanics' and Engineers' Book of Reference and Engineers' Field Book*, which was widely distributed and read. Even as late as 1881, specialty journals referred to the Gunter scale as "now common among intelligent workmen." Among other things, this implied that the general-purpose slide rule was not well known.

Research suggests that not until well after 1880 did even half of the engineering schools provide instruction regarding the use of slide rules. In 1881 Robert Riddell published his book *The Slide Rule Simplified*, but it described the older English Coggeshall scale system. [26]

However, Cox's articles in "Engineering News" around 1890 were crucial to the introduction of the Mannheim system in the United States, and the Mannheim slide rule became the standard. Cox patented several modifications of the Mannheim, and these modifications were produced by the subsequently famous firm of Keuffel & Esser. A later chapter on Keuffel & Esser will describe how this firm marketed slide rules that were very much ahead of their time.

Worth mentioning at this point is the early collaboration between K&E and the German manufacturer Dennert & Pape. The latter produced the first models that were sold in the U.S. by K&E. Later K&E produced its own slide rules.

After 1885 yet another American firm entered the picture. This was the Eugene Dietzgen Co., which operated as a mail-order business. At first (1887) Dietzgen sold imported slide rules, mainly from Germany and England, but later it manufactured its own slide rules.

In **Germany** the first evidence of slide rules appeared around the end of the 17th century, when Michael Scheffelt (1652-1720) described a slide rule that he developed. He was a teacher of mathematics at the very respected Building Guild School in Ulm, and his slide rule was described in his book *Pes mechanicus artificialis ...* (1699). He had already created quite a stir by building his own circle of proportions. However, *Pes mechanicus...* [27] served to call attention to the first German slide rule.

Scheffelt's slide rule was made of maple. It was four-sided (square in cross-section) and one meter long. Each side was covered with a layer of copper with 10 peculiar scales, one of which was further divided into four smaller scales. Settings and readings required (a) the use of dividers, in the same way that they are used with a Gunter scale, or (b) the use of adjustable leather straps.

Scheffelt's rule was later described by Jakob Leupold (1647-1727), advisor and mining commissioner for the King of Poland and the Prince of Saxony, in his book *Theatrum Arthmetico-Geometricum*, which was published shortly after his death. Leupold made it clear that he did not know who had invented this slide rule and that he had not seen other calculating devices of this type in use anywhere.

The slide rule acquired a modest degree of recognition from J. H. Lambert (1728-1777). In addition to his epoch-making work in other fields, this famous German astronomer, physicist, and mathematician devoted attention to the slide rule. From a work by Lambert [28] (further discussed later in this book), we learn that one of the few early German craftsmen to make slide rules was G.F. Brander (1713-1783), a famous instrument maker from Augsburg. He made a slide rule in accordance with Lambert's specifications, and for a long time this was the only German-made slide rule in use.

However, even this impetus from Lambert had only modest impact because Germany, as a nation, was so fragmented at that time. It would take over a hundred years before the slide rule achieved wide use here in the heart of Europe. This situation prevailed into the middle of the 1800s. The names of only a few of the Germans who wrote about slide rules are generally known, and the names of the craftsmen who made the few slide rules that were made, are almost forgotten. These craftsmen include Th. Baumann, C.T. Dörffel, and C.G. Grunow, all of Berlin. [29] The acceptance and interest in slide rules in Germany was quite different from that in nearby countries. For example, by the mid-1800s, schools in France, Italy, and Austro-Hungary were recommending use of the slide rule.

Only around the end of the 19th century and the establishment of a unified Germany, did the German slide rule begin its ascendancy. This was largely due to the domestic output of such firms as Dennert & Pape, A.W. Faber, Nestler, and later Reiss. Other makers such as Koch, Huxhold & Hannemann (Hamburg), AG Schröder (Darmstadt), and Schleicher & Schüll also deserve mention, although they were less significant in that they made few models and survived only briefly. It should also be noted that, compared to England, Germany had relatively few instrument makers at the end of the 19th century. However, structural improvements, new scale systems, and better quality soon secured a worldwide reputation for German products. This will be discussed in the chapter on "Makers and their Models."

Little is known about the early history of the slide rule in **Japan**. Only with the founding of the firm Hemmi did Japan begin its turbulent progress.

In summary, one can say that the history of the development of the slide rule in Europe coincides with the technical advances made in three European countries. The first was England, with its variety of models, especially the special purpose slide rules. Next was France after Napoleon I. Finally, there was Germany before the end of the 19th century. Also around the turn of the century, the Americans began to produce their own slide rules, and through the importation of American slide rules, the Japanese were stimulated to make their own.

More Men and Ideas

In England, as already mentioned, a large number of special purpose slide rules were made for applications related to navigation, surveying, the timber trades, and steam engines. These slide rules were produced by a large number of small instrument makers. Of course, in some cases the quality of the slide rules was disappointing. Only after ca. 1775 did the SOHO rules of James Watt set new standards of accuracy and achieve more functional scale arrangements.

In the subsequent years there were advances by such experts as the previously mentioned John Robertson (1712-1776). He devoted special attention to the task of modifying the Gunter scale for nautical calculations. He even tried to design a rule with sliding scales. He reported this in 1775 in his *Treatise on Mathematical Instruments*, which was published in London. After Robertson's death, his ideas were discussed further by his friend W. Mountaine in the pamphlet *A Description of the Lines drawn on Gunter's scale, as improved by Mr. John Robertson* (London, 1778). At that time the term "sliding Gunter rule" was coined for this type of nautical slide rule, and the older rules were grouped (especially in navigation) under the term "Gunter rule," or, especially in the case of seamen, "the Gunter."

From Mountaine until after World War II there were no writers (worth mentioning) who wrote about the introduction of the slide rule. After World War II, however, there was a dramatic increase in the number of books about slide rules (40 new titles). This extended to 1980, by which time the end of the slide rule era was already recognized.

From the second half of the 19th century on, the activities related to the introduction of the slide rule shifted mainly to continental Europe. As already mentioned, during this same time there was a trend toward slide rules designed to deal with the mathematical aspects of various technologies. Teachers in technical schools and professors in universities in the separate countries became the main advocates of these new aids to calculation.

In **France** the slide rule gained more acceptance after 1821 first as a result of rules imported from England and then later as a result of domestic production. The slide rule became well known through publications in the 1850s such as Leon Lalanne's *Instructions sur les règles à cálcul...* (1851) which was available in German and Spanish by 1852. Other important publications of the 1850s included Phillipp M. N. Benoit's *La règle à calcul expliquée, un Guide de...* (1855) and, last but not least, Amédée Mannheim's report *Règle à calcul modifiée* (1851). By this time calculation with the slide rule was already recommended in schools, which undoubtedly contributed to their wider adoption.

In **Italy** Quintinio Sella (1827-1884), Professor of Geometry at the University of Turin, joined the ranks of the famous advocates for the slide rule. He required his students to take a slide rule course, and he also published a textbook, *Teorica e Practica del Regolo Calcolatore* (1859). [30] This book achieved wide distribution and essentially advocated the adoption of Mannheim's slide rule. Indeed, it was Sella's book that first made Mannheim widely known in Italy. Sella also described a slide rule made by Gravet-Lenoir (Paris) which had two two-cycle scales (A/B), two one-cycle scales (C/D), a sine scale, and a tangent scale (in a model without a cursor!); in the floor of the stator (i.e., under the slide) there was a scale graduated in centimeters from 26 to 52. Sella described the scales thoroughly, and his descriptions were followed by numerous examples of their use and very clear diagrams of settings. Sella's work was followed by a book by R. Barbieri entitled *Regolo calcolatore* (Milan, 1900).

In the **Austro-Hungarian Empire** there were several experts who labored intensively to make the slide rule more widely known. Baron Adam von Burg (1797-1882), Professor of Mechanics and Engineering at the Polytechnical Institute of Vienna, mentioned slide rules in Sunday lectures concerning "popular topics." These lectures attracted large audiences. Also, Leopold Karl Schulz von Straßnitzki (1802-1852), a mathematician, gave Sunday lectures first in Laibach and later at the Polytechnical Institute in Vienna. He, too, sought to introduce calculation by slide rule, especially to craftsmen. He wrote a pamphlet entitled *Anleitung zum Gebrauch des englischen Rechenschiebers* (Guide to the use of English slide rules), and he developed a special slide rule for calculations related to construction. In his lectures he used a teaching aid [31] that had been invented by a Josef Adalbert Sedlacek (1785-1836). This device was the very first over-sized demonstration slide rule, and it is discussed further in a later chapter.

Sedlacek also promoted the use of the slide rule through lectures and articles. In one such source he said:

> "It is said that the use of the slide rule in England is so widespread that no tailor makes a pair of trousers without including a pocket just for carrying a 'sliding rule.' During such a time, it is difficult to understand why the slide rule does not enjoy such well-deserved recognition in our own country."

Sedkacek's lectures in the Austro-Hungarian capital had a very positive effect on the acceptance of the slide rule in this ethnically diverse empire at a time when the slide rule still lead a shadowy existence in the not-yet-unified Germany.

Another person who should be mentioned is Emil Herrmann (1840-1925). He was Professor of Mechanical Engineering at the Academy for Mining in Selmec and Oberbergrat. He wrote a textbook in Hungarian, *A szamtoloka (Règle à calcul),* that was published in 1879 in Budapest. Discussing the Mannheim system in his book, he named Calderoni & Co. in Pest as a source of this slide rule. This Italian firm is worth mentioning because, at that time, it served as a highly regarded distributor of teaching materials in various large European cities. Note that the slide rule that Herrmann recommended was French.

Around 1890 Karl von Ott, Special Professor at the Imperial German Technical School in Prague wrote a book titled *Der Logarithmische Rechenschieber – Theorie und Gebrauch desselben* (The Logarithmic Slide Rule – Theory and Use) and, thereby, recommended the use of the slide rule in yet another part of the Austro-Hungarian Empire. [32]

In **Russia,** in 1883, Professor Tscherepaschinski of the Moscow Polytechnical School published a slide rule textbook in Russian. As already mentioned, he concerned himself with a special arrangement of scales and had arranged for Tavernier-Gravet (Paris) to make a prototype. Also, he was connected with the German firm Nestler, which produced slide rules with his arrangement of scales.

Professor A. Hasselblatt of the Technical Institute in St. Petersburg developed a low-cost cardboard slide rule that most people could afford.

In **Germany** the slide rule was little used until the end of the 1800s. There was advice about the utility of the slide rule in Dingler's "Polytechnisches Journal" [33], but it did not bear much fruit. An important reason for this was the poor quality of the handmade slide rules produced at that time in Germany.

One of the first important German publications on the subject was *Der logarithmische Rechenschieber und sein Gebrauch* (The Logarithmic Slide Rule and Its Use), published in 1908 by Professor E. Hammer (1858-1925) of the Imperial Technical School at Stuttgart.[34] This book combined a painstaking study of the history of the slide rule, a discussion of some of the newer models and their makers, and a thorough user's guide. In a later publication, Hammer called *Theorie und Praxis des log. Rechenschiebers* by L. Schrutka von Rechtenstamm (1911) the first textbook about slide rules. In the category "popular technology" for foremen and craftsmen, Hammer mentioned the books by K. Treven (1913), J.E. Meyer (1913), and H.F.B. Schäfer (1916). In addition, Hammer, like many of his colleagues, commented frequently in the specialty journals about the new slide rule models that were appearing on the market, and the slide rule was briefly described in several general textbooks on mathematics.

Also, at this time, Rudolf Mehmke (1857-1944), Professor of Applied Mathematics at the Technical School in Stuttgart, was very actively engaged with matters relating to slide rules. He prepared the slide-rule-related chapter on "Numerical Calculations" in the *Enzyclopädie der Mathematischen Wissenschaften* (Encyclopedia of Mathematical Sciences) published by Teubner in Leipzig (1889-1904). Mehmke also wrote articles for the "Zeitschrift für Mathematik und Physik," a journal that he edited. Among these articles were ones in 1911 on "Rechenschieber in

Deutschland" (The Slide Rule in Germany) and on "SOHO-rules." Mehmke is also known as the inventor of a slide rule for chemists. [35]

From the turn of the century until the 1920s, articles related to slide rule usage appeared from time to time in the "Zeitschrift für Vermessungswesen" (Journal of Surveying). After the 1920s such articles appeared in the *Handbuch für Vermessungskunde* (Handbook of Surveying) published by the Metzlerschen Press. These articles continued through the 10th edition (1961), in which the newest slide rules and latest models were discussed. The emphasis, of course, was on special purpose slide rules of interest to surveyors.

Albert Rohrberg (1887-?), who ultimately served as headmaster in a secondary school in Berlin in the 1930s, has already been mentioned several times. Without doubt he deserves great credit for the increased use of the slide rule in Germany after World War I. His pamphlet *Theorie und Praxis des logarithmischen Rechenstabes* (Theory and Practice of the Logarithmic Slide Rule) appeared in 1916. In it he carefully considered the details of scales A, B, C, and D, the trigonometric scales S and T, the mantissa scale L, a log-log scale, and the scale that he labeled P (for Potenz – power). In the foreword to the 1929 edition of his very well-known book *Der Rechenstab im Unterricht aller Schularten* (The Slide Rule in Instruction at All Levels), [36] he noted that he had been commissioned by the ministers of instruction for several large cities in Germany to give lectures on the use of the slide rule. In addition he covered the topic in broadcasts from radio stations at Königswusterhausen, Breslau, Königsberg, and Bern. He lectured on slide rules used in commerce at the business schools in Berlin, Leipzig, and Nürnberg as well as at chambers of commerce and other business organizations. Sadly, now that the slide rule has been forgotten, the influence of Albert Rohrberg has also been forgotten.

After World War II the book *Der moderne Rechenstab* (The Modern Slide Rule) by Dr. Richard Stender found wide distribution. Essentially this book dealt with the ARISTO slide rules made by Dennert & Pape. First published in 1951, it went into several editions and an English edition, coauthored by McKelvey, also appeared.

The early publications in **North America** have already been mentioned. After 1900 it was mainly the suppliers of slide rules who became responsible for the increased use of the slide rule.

Among many other brochures offered by slide rule makers, Justin Hill's "A Course in the Slide Rule and Logarithms" (1943) assumed a special place. It was printed by the War Department in Washington DC especially for the armed services and included slide rules offered by Keuffel & Esser and by Dietzgen.

Regarding **Japan**, little is known. The most important event was the establishment of the SUN brand by Hemmi just at the close of the 19th century. Typically, slide rule literature was produced by the slide rule maker, thereby advancing the adoption of the slide rule. This same phenomenon was seen later in Europe.

The End of the Slide Rule Era

In 1967 the American firm Hewlett, Packard, using microprocessors that they had developed, produced the first pocket calculators. The first models to appear on the market were very primitive and still very expensive. They offered only the basic calculations (addition, subtraction, multiplication, and division) and were no threat to the slide rule. However, within just a few months, calculators with many more functions became available and prices began to drop. Even then the slide rule could still hold its own, especially in schools. However, after 1970 the slide rule was quickly superseded by the pocket calculator, and by 1975 the "tool of the engineer," the "favorite of millions," and the "nightmare of many students" reached the end of its centuries-long usefulness.

Technical Aspects of the Slide Rule

Patents and Related Issues

Patent protection for slide rules was sought early. A patent for a circular slide rule was granted to Delamaine around 1630 and the first English patents for slide rules were awarded in the 17th and 18th centuries. In 1851 Nystrom obtained a U.S. patent for his circular slide rule. Keuffel & Esser's first patent was granted in 1881 for the Thacher cylinder rule. The first important German patent relating to slide rules was obtained in 1886, for the application of white celluloid veneer scales to wooden rules.

However, in the case of slide rules the protection offered by patents was often virtually meaningless. One way or another, the patents of one maker were evaded by other makers. This was especially true of patents relating to design. The competition would adopt the patent holder's basic idea but would build the slide rule in a way that did not technically violate the patent. In the case of new scales based on mathematical concepts, like Roget's log-log scales (for which no patent application was actually made), innovations were directly copied, or elaborated upon, by other makers.

As we know, all this began with Gunter's magnificent invention of logarithms and continued with Oughtred's sliding rulers, Partridge's double-sided slide rule and Mannheim's cursor (none of which were patented). In case after case people found opportunities to take these basic concepts, apply them in new ways, and offer them as their own ideas.

For example, the celluloid scale patented by Dennert & Pape (see DRP #34583, Appendix I) was an extremely far-reaching idea. As is often the case with epoch-making innovations, the idea was very simple. Before the celluloid scale was introduced, virtually all slide rules had to be made of a pale yellow wood, i.e., boxwood, so that the black scale marks would be readable. In 1870 the American, Hyatt, invented celluloid. Dennert & Pape succeeded in glueing a celluloid strip to the stator by paying careful attention to the expansion coefficients of the two parts. Within a few years all other makers copied this technique, which had the great advantage of permitting them to use other suitable (but darker) kinds of wood. Mahogany, Swiss pearwood, and Japanese bamboo became the main materials used to carry the celluloid scales.

What did Dennert & Pape get out of its patent for celluloid scales? Virtually nothing! It was simply not possible to achieve world-wide patent protection of the celluloid scale. Perhaps this outcome was also due to the fact that D&P had obtained a patent for celluloid scales on rulers, but not on slide rules. Otherwise D&P might have made a fortune through licensing fees. Many other inventors in the slide rule world met with similar fates.

However, there were a few cases where patent protection was important. For example, in the U.S. the patents obtained from 1891-1900 by K&E (and its consultant William Cox) for the duplex slide rule were quite effective. These patents secured a decisive and long-lasting advantage for the maker and the brand name.

It should also be appreciated that there were some national differences in patent protection. In most countries patents were granted to the manufacturer or individual inventors for structural improvements of slide rules or new scale arrangements. However, in Germany scale arrangements could not be patented. Sometimes it was possible to get a registered design (DRGM). These were sought if the idea did not justify a patent or the improvement did not justify the costs of obtaining a patent.

There were other interesting trends regarding patents. For example, the German Patent Tables in this book (see Appendix I.) illustrate that greater emphasis was placed on German patent protection before World War II than after World War II. Also, certain manufacturers, especially Faber (later Faber-Castell) and Nestler seemed to place more importance on patent protection than did other makers. (Patents and their protection were even declared in early catalogs and product information, but this kind of "publicity" was scarcely seen after World War II.) It is also clear that few of the individual inventors of patented slide rule improvements had the good fortune to find someone to actually manufacture their inventions.

Obvious as well was that German patents – and perhaps all patents – saw very few additional improvements in the structure of the slide rule after World War II. New slide rule models (i.e., new "products") were subsequently created by increasing the number and kinds of scales on slide rules, but these changes did not gain patent protection.

Appendix I provides a list of German patents and registered designs relating to slide rules. For a detailed list of American, English, and other European patents the reader is referred to Peter Hopp's book [37]. Also worth mentioning is an article by Robert K. Otnes [38] that includes a description of individual K&E patents as well as a thorough history of the firm.

Stators and Slides

As we have seen, the form of the slide rule had not progressed very far prior to the middle of the 19th century. Gunter's scale was followed by the "sliding Gunter" and then by Partridge's development of the "true slide rule," with only a few other minor improvements made thereafter.

At that time one-sided slide rules consisted of a stator with a movable slide and a cursor that moved in grooves. In some cases, especially before the cursor was invented, there were slide rules with several slides. Again, in some cases, round or oval windows with index lines were created in the back of the stator so that the scales on the back of the slide could be used to make settings or read results. To accommodate additional scales, some older forms had even longer windows in the floor of the stator. For example, in the case of System Pickworth, there was a long oval window which had on its beveled lower edge the first cycle (1-10) of the cubic scale. This system was patented in 1909 by C. N. Pickworth (DRP 215722), and A. W. Faber produced two slide rules (Models 374 and 384) with System Pickworth.

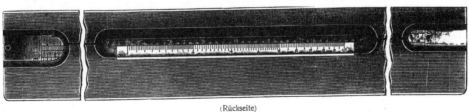

(Rückseite)

Fig.11. Back of Pickworth slide rule

Around the turn of the 20th century, the definitive form of **the two-sided (duplex) slide rule** was invented in America. This form had a cursor that permitted the user to make settings on one side of the slide rule and readings on the other. (US Patent 460930, 1891, by Cox). The duplex stator consisted of two sections which were connected by metal (later plastic) straps. The slide moved between the two sections of the stator in grooves, and the "wrap-around" cursor covered both sides of the slide rule.

In the case of **one-sided slide rules**, the period from the turn of the century until the 1920s was noteworthy for the special efforts that manufacturers took to make structural improvements in the slide rule. For example, a critical issue was the stabilization of the stator and slide in order to prevent twisting and bending due to atmospheric conditions or mechanical influences. With this goal in mind, in 1908 A.W. Faber began to incorporate metal bands or strips in all wooden slide rules. These bands were placed edgewise and longitudinally in the stator, and vertical strips were incorporated in some slides. This innovation was protected by patent (DRP 206428, 1907). Also, special efforts were made very early on to make sure that the slide moved as smoothly as possible. Stators for one-sided slide rules were no longer made as one piece. The stator was cut lengthwise and then the two pieces were bound together with a flat sheet of celluloid or, later, metal. The result was a spring effect that assured smooth slide action.

As early as 1901, Dennert & Pape obtained a patent (DRP 126499) for a springy celluloid sheet that was built into the floor of the stator. A.W. Faber accomplished the same thing by connecting the two halves of the stator with a celluloid strip that was glued between layers in the floor of the stator (DRGM 306107 in 1907). Later the celluloid was replaced by a springy metal grid (DRGM 522689 in 1912). Early in the 1970s plans were made to incorporate this same springy metal grid in plastic slide rules, with the spring inserted during the injection molding stage of production.

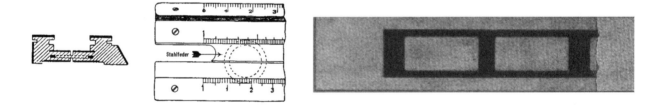

Fig.12. Tension springs in slide rule stators

Nestler had a similar system. At first a strip of rubber or celluloid was glued into the stator floor (DRP 173660 in 1905). Later Nestler, too, switched to metal springs. In its models, the springs were metal rings which were glued at intervals into the stator floor and served to connect the two halves of the stator (DRP 410565 in 1924). All the other manufacturers ultimately imitated this construction. For example, instead of celluloid or metal springs, SUN-Hemmi substituted an aluminum sheet that was glued and screwed into place.

In the case of the "super long" (50 cm) single-sided slide rules, there was yet a further structural improvement. These slide rules were equipped with up to four, vertically directed, adjustment screws which were distributed along the entire length of the slide rule in order to hold the two halves of the stator together. If necessary, these screws could be used to adjust the space between the two halves. If the spring in the stator floor was bent too frequently or inexpertly, the spring effect could be impaired, causing a gap between important scales on the slide-stator interface and making exact reading across these scales difficult. The adjustment screws were used to remedy this problem, as well as to regulate the smoothness of the slide action. (Dennert & Pape DRGM 192052 in 1903, and Faber-Castell DRP 365637 in 1922).

To some extent, this system of adjustment screws was adopted for pocket models. The result was a rather high and unnecessary degree of quality.

After a slide rule was used for a long time, the ends of the laminated celluloid scales often became unglued. In addition to the glue, A.W. Faber used small, tapered, hardwood pins to fasten the scales onto their slide rules (DRGM 371190, 1908-1909). Nestler used nickel silver screws (DRGM 164885). Even some SUN-Hemmi slide rules had celluloid scales secured by light metal pins.

The double-sided slide rules were adjustable within their metal bars or strap-joints, and this permitted improvement of their slide action. The holes in the stator, through which the strap-joint screws ran, were oval. Therefore, by loosening the strap-joint screws, one could adjust the distance between the stator rails and restrict or relax the slide action. Once the adjustment was satisfactory, it could be retained by tightening the screws. (e.g., Adolf W. Keuffel's U.S. Patent 1930852 in 1933 and A.W. Faber-Castell's DBP 873455 in 1951). Of course such adjustment was not possible in the case of the glued strap-joints found in plastic double-sided slide rules (e.g., Aristo, Graphoplex, Nestler, and Faber-Castell's school models, among others).

Cursors

As already noted, the cursor was one of the decisive improvements conceived (or rediscovered) by Amédée Mannheim as a young student and incorporated in the slide rule named after him. The cursor made it possible to carry out calculations using scales that were not immediately adjacent. The cursor also made it possible to interpolate better between marks on a scale and, thereby, achieve more precision. As mentioned earlier, Isaac Newton (with his "hairline") and John Robertson were the first to use the cursor. Around 1837 the Frenchman Mouzin mentioned a "setting device" made of copper, which could be used to establish settings and read results. [39] However, only after Mannheim's publication did the cursor establish itself, through ongoing improvements, as an indispensable component of the slide rule.

As a rule, the cursors around the end of the 19th century were made of blackened brass plate. These cursors could be used to make settings and read results using narrow flanges or "noses" that projected to the left (as introduced by Mannheim in 1850) or both right and left (as offered by Dennert & Pape in 1872).

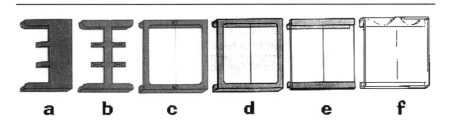

a. One-sided wedge cursor
b. Two-sided wedge cursor
c. Cursor with hair as index
d. Cursor with etched index
e. Free view cursor
f. Plastic cursor

Fig.13. Cursor designs "A - F"

What evolved thereafter were framed cursors. The first ones actually had a hair for a hairline. Later (in 1889) A. W. Faber introduced framed cursors with a tiny glass window glued into the frame. One or more hairlines were scratched on the underside of the window and blackened with lamp-black. Of course the frame edges bothered the user when the cursor was used to read results. This led to the so-called "frameless" cursor. These had only narrow rims at the top and bottom of the glass window; these rims engaged with grooves in the stator. A leaf spring was fastened in the upper rim. When the rim was pressed down from above, this spring provided a certain flexibility that made the back and forth movement of the cursor easier.

Around 1920, pocket slide rules were offered with clear celluloid cursors that had upper and lower edges that were bent inward. In the case of the normally constructed cursors, holes were drilled through the window, and aluminum guides were attached by screws. On these aluminum guides tiny additional small windows were installed. These windows were used for settings and readings involving scales on the upper and lower slanted edges of the slide rule (See, for example, Nestler's DRP 650558, 1935).

Framed cursors with glass windows were offered through the end of the 1930s. Double-sided cursors for duplex slide rules were designed with glass windows up to the end of the slide rule era, especially in the U.S. and Japan.

For a long time (at least through its 1940 catalog) the cursors for one-sided SUN-Hemmi slide rules had a very characteristic form. The metal frame was open on the left, and the glass window was displaced to the left. As a result of this, the right hand, which held and moved the cursor, did not cover the window. (Of course left-handed users had a problem with this cursor.)

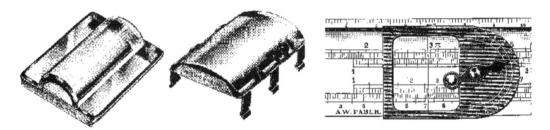

Fig.14. Cursor designs (Hemmi and Faber)

Another peculiarity was the cursor with an "indicator" for determining the number of decimal places in the result. This cursor was introduced by A. W. Faber in 1905. On the right side of the cursor there was a semicircular extension with a scale running from –6 through 0 to +6. The purpose of this scale was to keep track of the decimal point. Slide rules with this cursor also had special notations at the ends of the upper and lower scales. The lower scale on the stator was marked "Quotient +1" at the beginning and "Product –1" at the end. The upper scale on the stator was marked ←⁺⌐₊→ at both ends. In the case of multiplication, one determined the number of decimal places in the product by adding the number of decimal places in the two individual factors and subtracting 1 whenever the result was read to the right of the first factor, i.e., the factor on the lower scale. If the product was read to the left of the first factor, then the sum of the decimal places was used unchanged. The markings "Quotient +1", etc., were added as "reminders." The system was clever but much too complicated. This kind of cursor was essentially abandoned (by Faber-Castell) before World War I. Surprisingly, an "indicator cursor" appears in the SUN-Hemmi catalogs as late as 1940.

The most important thing about the cursor was the hairline. With the help of the hairline, one could get tighter control of the process of calculating and use two scales that were not adjacent. American and Japanese cursors were usually equipped with only one hairline.

Almost without exception, slide rules made in Europe until the early 1930's had cursors with two supplementary hairlines to the right and left of the central index line. These were used to convert the cross-sectional area of a circle to the diameter. There were also two shorter lines for conversion of kilowatts to horsepower on the Continent (1 KW = 1.36 PS) and in the United Kingdom and United States (1 KW = 1.34 HP).

These cursor markings were assigned especially great importance in Germany in the 1920s and 1930s. This emphasis on cursor markings, plus the greatly inflated assortment of slide rule makers, resulted in a situation where, in many cases, two different models differed only in the number of lines on the cursor.

Slide rules with the "merchant's system" had a short index mark to the left of the central hairline. When using this system to calculate interest, this short mark indicated exactly 365 days when the main hairline was set at 360.

One curiosity was the Cardugramm cursor (DRGM, 1935). This was used with an "endless weight table" for weight estimation based on cross-section and could be added to a normal cursor. Although well conceived, the cursor did not gain acceptance and disappeared from the market.

Another noteworthy idea was the Goulding cursor. Baxandall [40] describes it as follows:

> "This is designed for mechanically dividing small spaces between the divisions on a slide rule, in order to obtain the third or fourth figure of reading more accurately than by the quicker and more usual method of estimation. The reading marks of the cursor can be made to slide a variable distance in the cursor frame by means of a lever. This lever passes over an angular scale divided into ten parts, and carries a sliding pointer, which can be adjusted so as to pass over the whole of the scale while the reading mark passes over the space to be divided." [40]

The Goulding cursor was too expensive to make and too difficult to use. It did not survive long.

Magnifying cursors appeared by the beginning of the 1900s. In 1909, A. W. Faber patented the "periscopic" magnifying cursor (DRP 222297). It had two polished lenses mounted on a swivel joint attached to one side of the lens frame. The lens could be swung around to read the underside of the slide rule.

All the important slide rule makers offered magnifying cursors. The American Keuffel & Esser had two types of "magnifiers," a "single" with one lens, and a "double" with two lenses. These magnifiers could be attached to the cursors and were easily removed. Dietzgen had an attachable semi-cylindrical lens, and a "magnifier" with only one lens.

In the beginning, magnifying cursors were round polished lenses mounted in metal frames. Later the lenses were rectangular. The magnifying lenses were attached to the cursor with supports made of wire or metal. These supports were placed on the cursor frame, slipped onto the frame, or fastened to it with screws. Most of these supports could be collapsed (either while on the slide rule or after removal) for transport.

After 1960 there were lenses of extruded plexigum. Some of these, too, could be folded down while mounted on the slide rule (e.g., Faber-Castell 52L).

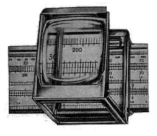

Fig.15. Cursor designs (Faber-Castell)

Nestler was the first to achieve a similar effect by cementing half-cylinder lenses on the cursor window. Admittedly this cursor provided less magnification, and the area that was in focus was narrower.

Dennert & Pape, A.W. Faber, and other makers also adopted this design. Later Faber arranged for the half-cylinder lens to slide along the cursor (DRP 450304, 1926). Thus the lens could be used to magnify areas lateral to the central hairline, e.g., when reading results off the supplementary index lines.

With the introduction of injection-molded plastics after the Second World War, the low-cost mass-production of ideally designed, virtually indestructible, frameless cursors became possible. In the last years of the slide rule era, cursor windows were often made slightly convex, resulting in some magnification and some brightening effect. These cursors were sold without the extra charge usually associated with magnifying cursors.

Of course, through the end of the slide rule era, cursors with flat glass windows and metal frames were the rule in the U.S. and Japan. In these countries, injection molding techniques were not applied to cursor production. After the mid-1950s, however, German makers offered only such injection-molded plastic cursors.

Materials for Making Stators and Slides

At first, and for a long time, boxwood was the preferred material for slide rules. The natural yellow-brown color formed the background for the scale marks and the numbers which were incised in the wood and blackened. Boxwood was especially well suited to this use because of the wood's denseness and uniform coloring. A slide rule collector can safely assume that almost any boxwood slide rule without celluloid scales was made before 1907.

However, as early as the 1700s English makers were using brass or mahogany in some cases. For example, David Baxandall [41] lists a 20 cm long slide rule of brass that was made by Troughton of London in 1791. At that time brass was the preferred material for navigation instruments of all kinds.

Also of interest are individual slide rules with a boxwood stator and a brass slide, e.g., a 60 cm long device made in 1917 by the J. Rabone firm of Birmingham, England. [42]

Mahogany was also used early on, but it was less well suited because of its very dark color. However, mahogany experienced a renaissance after the introduction of celluloid veneer for die-stamped scales. From then on mahogany was used for all high quality and expensive slide rules.

For example, Nestler, Dennert & Pape, and Keuffel & Esser used mahogany with celluloid overlay either exclusively or for a long time.

Ivory was rarely used, though ivory slide rules of various types were made in the 17th and 18th centuries, especially in England, and ivory slide rules with scale lengths of 12.5, 20, and 25 cm were offered by Nestler as late as 1912. These slide rules had the four principal scales of the time.

Toward the end of the 1800s boxwood, mahogany, and then pear wood were the leading materials; later, around the mid-1920s, mahogany and pear wood prevailed, with occasional slide rules made of ebony. Sometimes beech wood or some other lower quality wood was used for school, and other lower-priced, slide rules. We find these materials used by Unique, Reiss, and Meissner, and Faber-Castell used them after W.W. II when Swiss pear wood could not be imported.

Only the Japanese chose to make slide rules of bamboo, a material that is especially well suited for use in slide rules. Bamboo slide rules offered on the American market by Post, Dietzgen, etc., were of Japanese origin.

Thus pear wood and mahogany became accepted as the preferred material when, toward the end of the 1800s, Dennert & Pape introduced its epoch-making innovation – the wooden slide rule with celluloid scales (DRP 34583) in 1886. On this white background material, scale markings of black or other colors were very easy to see and to read. As already mentioned, this contrast had not heretofore been achieved with the use of the relatively dark natural woods (with the exception of boxwood).

During the last 10 years of the slide rule era a further refinement in materials was introduced at Faber-Castell, i.e., laminated wood (Preß-Schichtholz). This involved paper-thin layers of wood that were pressed and then glued together.

Another important material used for slide rules was anodized light metal, particularly aluminum. Certain firms, such as Ecobra and Pickett & Eckel, specialized in anodized slide rules. Other makers, for example Reiss and Mouzin (France), offered metal slide rules at one time or another.

Celluloid, the first thermoplastic synthetic material, was a mixture of cellulose nitrate and camphor. It was invented by J. W. Hyatt (1837-1920). He obtained the U.S. patent (Nr. 105338) for "Celluloid" in 1870. He and his brother produced and sold this plastic, and its first application was as a dental material. Later it was used for billiard balls, for combs, and as a base for the first photographic film. Last but not least, celluloid was eminently suited for use as a surface for wooden slide rules (acknowledging, of course, that the material did tend to become yellow after long exposure to light.). In the 1920s and 1930s, pocket slide rules were first made of a celluloid-covered, wooden core and later out of solid celluloid.

In 1913 the German chemists F. Klatte and E. Zacharias received a patent (DRP 281877) for the polymerization of vinylchloride to polyvinylchloride (PVC). The further development of PVC was held back by World War I; however, in the 1920s the technical development of the process was undertaken by I.G. Farben at its plants in Rheinfelden, Bitterfeld, and Ludwigshafen. This undertaking was successful, and around 1933 a vinylchloride-maleic-acid-diethylester copolymerisate was developed in Ludwigshafen. This was brought into production by Dynamit-Nobel, AG (DNAG), a subsidiary of I.G. Farben, and marketed as ASTRALON.

The first slide rules to be made completely of Astralon were produced in 1936 by Dennert & Pape. The stators and slides were milled from flat sheets of Astralon. Dennert & Pape also gradually replaced celluloid with Astralon as a veneer for wooden slide rules, i.e., thin strips of cut Astralon were glued to the upper surface of the stator and slide. Around this same time most other makers switched from celluloid to Astralon. Soon after the Second World War, the applications for plastic materials grew rapidly. This growth was supported by improved manufacturing techniques. There followed a transition to the manufacture of slide rules by the injection molding process, and the mechanical process of milling the stator and slide could be abandoned. The new, impact-resistant polystyrol was much better suited for injection molding than was PVC. It was merely a matter of adding elastomers (styrol-butadiene-rubber) to attain an extraordinarily high ductility. When this plastic was used for slide rules, considerable white pigment was added in order to guarantee good color contrast when the scales were stamped on the slide rule. One-sided slide rules made of wood were now joined by one-sided slide rules made of plastic. This was also true for pocket slide rules. Also, the great age of double-sided slide rules now began in Europe because injection molding was nothing short of ideal for making this type of rule. It was no longer necessary to assemble wooden parts. Now one injection process produced both stator rails (complete with grooves) and the slide (with flanges).

The large firms manufacturing slide rules came up with their own new names for this plastic: *Anag*it (**A**lbert **N**estler **AG**), *Aristo*pal (**Aristo** – Dennert & **Pa**pe), *Gero*plast (Faber-Castell Werk, **Gero**ldsgrün), Microglide (Dietzgen), and Ivorite (K&E).

Two German firms (Faber-Castell and Nestler), the Japanese, and the Americans preferred to join the stator rails with metal bars, while Dennert & Pape went forward with its invention, i.e., bars of plastic that were glued or welded onto the stator, without doubt a more economical process. DIWA, Graphoplex, and others also adopted this technique. It was also used by Faber-Castell and Nestler for their "beginners" slide rules (Schul-Rechenschieber).

At this point it might helpful to review briefly how wooden slide rules were manufactured. The methods described below were used at Faber-Castell. The preferred material was Swiss pear wood, which is a hard wood with fine pores. The wood was supplied as raw trunks. It was cut into boards and subjected to a long treatment with steam. After that the wood was air-dried for two years. This was followed by further drying in a room with precisely controlled humidity. The wood was then cut with milling machines so that the pieces had the shape and the dimensions required for the slide rule. The stator and the slide were produced separately. In order to achieve the stability that was required later, metal reinforcing was inserted. The highest quality inserts were of brass, but steel or aluminum inserts were used during wartime or post-war shortages of brass. Next the surface of the wood was roughed up, and a white celluloid veneer was glued to the slide and stator. The unfinished slide rules were then stored for a while in clamps, after which the upper surface was polished and cleaned. The slide was turned over so that both sides were smoothed; this assured that no expansion or shrinkage could occur, and that the rule was protected against warping. Now the scales could be imprinted on the celluloid. Then the cursor was mounted on the slide rule and the finished product was given a final inspection. The above description of the manufacturing process is, in fact, highly condensed; producing a slide rule typically required over 100 separate operations.

Scale Dividing and Manufacturing Methods

Reports are not available about the hand methods used for making slide rules in England in the first decades of the 17th century. Nevertheless there must have been some very productive and experienced craftsmen, who could produce very functional wooden slide rules. What is remarkable is that these craftsmen could divide the scales and incise the markings so accurately. In this context it is astonishing to note that, in information provided in 1866 by the English rule maker Rabone, we learn that a Gunter line with 540 marks could be scored by hand in 10 minutes.

One report of a rule-making establishment in Germany comes from a booklet by Professor J. H. Lambert (1728-1777), who is also said to have worked on the improvement of the Gunter scale. Lambert wrote in his "Preliminary Report" that he intended his treatise to be a collection of short papers on mathematics. However, he left the math out, and devoted the treatise to his slide rule.

By chance Lambert had come in contact with the famous German instrument maker Brander who was engaged, in 1761, to build a prototype of Lambert's rule. This prototype was one meter long, very precise, and very legible. Like Wingate's slide rule, Brander's was comprised of two rules which slid against each other. However, the greater requirements of this device soon necessitated a more advanced dividing technology. Here the English instrument maker Jesse Ramsden (1735-1800) succeeded as a pioneer in this field. During a long developmental period between 1760 and 1773 he constructed the first dividing machine. He reached an agreement with the Board of London, which allowed publication of a detailed description of his apparatus in exchange for a fee.

There were many successors. Among these Edward Troughton (1753-1835) deserves special mention. The catalog of the Science Museum in London makes reference to a slide rule made by him dated 1791.

Etienne Lenoir (1744-1832) and his son Paul Etienne M. Lenoir (1776-1827) were, in their time, well known and highly regarded makers of surveying instruments in Paris. Among other distinctions, they provided instruments for Napoleon's army in Egypt, and Paul Lenoir took part in that campaign. In 1814 Etienne Lenoir was named the Engineer to the King (Louis XVIII). Around 1821, Etienne Lenoir, using drawings by Jamard and Collaudeau, constructed a dividing machine which scored the markings for eight scales 25 cm long. [43] When Etienne, who survived his son, died, the firm's name changed to Gravet-Lenoir. Later the firm became Tavernier-Gravet, or in some cases Tavernier-Vinay.

In England the firm W.F. Stanley & Co. Ltd. had made a name for itself as a maker of mathematical and surveying instruments since 1853. W. F. Stanley himself (1829-1909) received more than 80 patents and was clearly the most important instrument maker in his country. In 1861, Stanley developed a dividing machine for linear scales and used the machine to mark the scales on the measuring rules and surveying devices that Stanley made, although among Stanley's total offering of 3000 items of this kind, slide rules certainly represented a very small fraction.

Until the end of the 1800s these makers and their trademarks were top-ranking in Europe.

By the end of the 1800s, however, successors to these first dividing machines (of Ramsden, Lenoir, and Stanley) were being developed by manufacturers in Germany, the U.S., and Japan. This new generation of dividing machines would score mark by mark – short and long – at logarithmic intervals with great precision. These were "multiple" dividing machines, i.e., they would mark identical scales simultaneously on several slide rules. After the marks were made, the numbers were impressed or stamped on the scales. Finally, the scale markings and the numbers were pigmented.

Figure 16A (on the next page) shows the dividing and application of numbers to individual slide rules at Dennert & Pape in 1912. Figure 16B shows a "20 arm" dividing machine at the same firm in 1962. This machine, which employed a "pantographic method," could score the scales on 20 slide rules at the same time.

During the 1920s, A.W. Faber took a different course. Using a precision milling machine, the logarithmic scale markings of one or two parallel scales were cut into a block of brass of the corresponding length. Next a tiny steel blade was wedged into the slot at each scale mark.

Fig.16A. Scale marking and numbering at D & P in 1912

Fig.16B. Dividing machine at D & P in 1962

Inaccuracies would arise through this wedging process, so each blade was checked by the logarithmic milling machine and, if necessary, adjusted. Numerals and letters were added as pieces of type that were inserted in spaces milled out at the appropriate locations.

The resulting "dividing block," with its single scale or scale-pair, would then be arranged with others to create the device for a whole scale system. Thus, during manufacture, all the scales in an entire scale system could be impressed on the slide rule in one operation.

Fig.17. Scale marking tool or die (System Darmstadt) from Faber-Castell

After the scales were cut on the slide rule, green, red, or black coloring was rubbed into the interval marks, the numbers, and the letters by an abrasive belt. Finally a wet polishing technique (using an abrasive belt combined with flowing water) was applied to the upper surfaces to assure an absolutely polished and smooth surface.

This was a rational and highly effective procedure; its development and optimization, however, succeeded only after great difficulties and after considerable expense in fabricating the dividing block. Faber-Castell started the above scale-dividing method for wooden slide rules around 1920, after a long period of testing and experimental series. From 1952 on, plastic slide rules were also finished in this same way. [44] (Models in unusual sizes were divided in another way. See the photochemical method below.) Dennert & Pape began using the dividing block process in 1935 when it started using Astralon, although some types of its slide rules were still divided by multiple dividing machines.)

Beginning around 1948, school slide rules (the very successful Scholar series) were divided by a similar method called the "foil-printing process" or the "hot press process." Here too a dividing block was used, but the red and black filling of the engraved lines and letters was accomplished by laying on pigmented strips. This pigmented material was similar to typewriter carbon paper. It was cut to suitable sizes and used only once. The die was pressed into the slide rule's surface and after the impression, the pigmented strip was laid in position and the second pressing was done with heat. The hot block process resulted in a finely ridged surface that was not as smooth as the surface left by the dividing engine process.

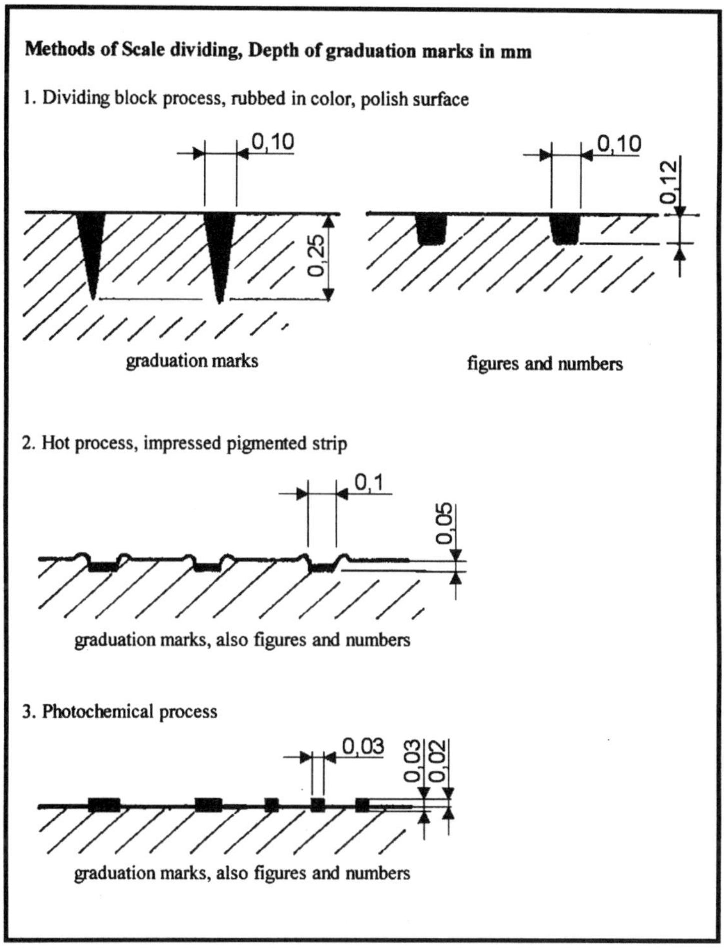

While Thornton used the dividing block process after 1947, eventually most slide rule makers (including the U.S. makers, Nestler, and Sun-Hemmi) used multiple dividing machines. Nestler, for example, had seven logarithmic dividing machines with sixteen dividing heads on each machine. These machines were capable of making 60-70 strokes per minute.

All slide rules that were cut with dividing machines (i.e., the "pantographic" method) as well as those cut by dividing block (Faber-Castell, and later Thornton and D&P) were labeled (but not stamped) "engine divided." This label was required, especially in the U.S., and constituted a certificate of quality.

Even more rational methods were being developed whereby the slide rule slug, or "blank," with scales already impressed by the mold, was produced by the die-injection machine. It appears that this method was not widely adopted, but we know that the K&E Decilon (c. 1960) was made this way. [45].

Fig.17A. Methods of scale dividing

The **photochemical methods** of manufacture employed a **master-copy** ("Urfolie") that was made on photographic film. This master-copy preserved the whole scale system for the model that was to be made. All the scale marks were cut in by a precise dividing machine, colored black, and then polished smooth. Numbers and letters were made by photomontage and etched into the film and blackened. There was a separate master-copy for the front and the reverse. The film had to be stable enough in the vertical and horizontal directions to minimize, as much as possible, inaccuracies that might develop over time or with repeated use. Master copies were stored under conditions of stable temperature and were only used to make working copies.

In order to make the photochemical process of production economical, the scale system for a whole slide rule was transferred several times (depending on the slide rule's size) to a transparent **working copy** ("Nutzen") which fit in a standardized copy frame that accepted sheets 60 x 70 cm. Thus a working copy could be used to make several slide rules at the same time.

The photochemical **production process** involved 60 x 70 cm sheets of material, usually Astralon, which were 3mm thick for pocket slide rules and 10mm thick for most other models. These sheets of Astralon were treated with a fluid, light-sensitive material. Because of the size of these sheets and the need to achieve an absolutely uniform coat of light-sensitive material, the light-sensitive material was applied while the sheets of Astralon were rotated rapidly in a horizontal plane. The light-sensitive material was added at the center of rotation and allowed to spread over the 60 x 70 sheets by centrifugal force.

The slide rule images were transferred to the treated Astralon in the following way: A sheet of Astralon was placed in a copy frame with the light-sensitive side up. Next the transparent working copy was placed on top of the Astralon with slide rule images on the underside against the light-sensitive surface on the Astralon. Next came a glass plate which sealed the light box. A vacuum was applied to bring the light-sensitive coating and the working copy into tight contact. Next a very powerful carbon-arc lamp was used to shine light through the working copy onto the light-sensitive coating of the Astralon. The light hardened the light-sensitive coating where it was not shielded by the images on the working copy. Next the Astralon sheet was removed from the light box, and corrosive dye was applied to the hardened surface. (If both black and red scales were required, templates were used when applying the two dyes.) Because the coating remained soft where it was not exposed to light, the dye penetrated these areas and colored the underlying Astralon. Next the entire coating was washed away with water leaving the images of the slide rule scales on the sheet of Astralon.

Fig.18. Photochemical process at Faber-Castell

There followed the usual mechanical process of slide rule making. Following this step, the sheets could be processed further by cutting out the slide rules, which were now defined by their (now-visible) scale markings. These individual pieces could be sawed, milled, and polished. Next the cursors were applied, and the end product was inspected. This same process was even followed for the massive demonstration slide rules.

The above brief description of the individual steps in the process merely touches on the numerous and complicated production steps in this important production sector. Moreover, many of these steps are among the maker's best-kept trade secrets. This description is only intended to round out the overall picture of slide rule era.

Scales, Scale Systems, and their Significance

If one looks closely at the arrangement of scales and scale markings over the centuries, one will notice many changes from the time of the Gunter scale to the time of the modern slide rule.

All slide rules were classified according to their scale length, usually the basic C/D scales. The effective length was considered to be the distance from 1 to 10 on scales C and D. (The short extensions beyond 1 and 10 were ignored.) Catalogs generally classified slide rules in this way, too.

If we start with Gunter's slide rule, which was 2 feet (60 cm) long, we see that the following standard scale lengths evolved:

- Pocket models: 10 cm, 12.5 cm (the second most popular size of all slide rules), 15 cm, and 20 cm.
- Standard models: 25 cm (by far the most popular size), 36 cm, and 40 cm
- Desk Models: 50 cm, 60 cm, 100 cm.

Of course, we should add to this list the demonstration or "class room" slide rules, with scales that were 1 to 2 meters long. Along with this increase in length came thicker, more readable, scale marks and numbers.

Lengths other than those listed above were very unusual.

American- and English-made slide rules tended to deviate slightly from the standard metric lengths and conform to the corresponding lengths in inches. For example, the American and English "10 inch" slide rule could be 25.4 cm (not 25.0 cm) long from 1 to 10 on scales C and D.

Until the 20th century, scales followed, almost without exception, the so-called **"railroad track" format**. In other words, the vertical scale-interval marks were bounded at the top and bottom by two continuous horizontal lines. In some cases a double horizontal line was used to demark intervals with values of 5 or 10. In the beginning, this format made it substantially easier to transfer distances when using pointed dividers, as well as making it easier to evaluate intervals. Later this format was carried over to slide rules, and was continued even after the introduction of the cursor. Here the "railroad track" format was especially useful when using the cursor hairline that crossed several scales, because the format made it easier to interpolate when making settings or reading results (except perhaps on pocket models). In the last 10 years of the slide rule era, the horizontal lines were generally abandoned, and slide rules were made with vertical lines only. Here the innovators were the Americans and Japanese.

The **scale designations** (that usually appeared at the left end of each scale) also had a long evolution, which culminated in the generally applied A,B,C,D, etc. Early in the 1950s, mathematical symbols such as "sin 0.1 x" (i.e., sine scale S) were added at the right end of many scales.

The beginnings of the scale names and positions that ultimately became standard are to be found in the English SOHO rules at the end of the 1700s. Recall that the scale sequence on the SOHO rule was A/B, C/D. In this case the A, B, and C scales were two-cycle scales (1-100) and only the D scale was a one-cycle scale (1-10). A two-cycle C scale was still necessary because there was no cursor; therefore it was not yet possible to use the hairline to read on C the square root of a number on A (and vice versa).

In the following period there were many special scales, and the position of the basic scales varied. The English slide rules before 1900 are representative of these trends. However, after 1851, certain "standard features," which eventually virtually all slide rules exhibited, gained force, namely the scale system of Amédée Mannheim. These standard features were: two two-cycle scales (A/B) and two one-cycle scales (C/D) on the front of the slide rule; the trigonometric functions on the back of the slide; and the cursor (which Mannheim reintroduced).

Fig.19. M. Rietz (1872-1956)

The next important step was made in 1902 by the German engineer Max Rietz when he added the K (cube) scale and the linear L ("log," or more correctly mantissa) scale. With the addition of two further improvements (i.e., the inverted CI scale in 1925 and the ST scale for small angles) the classic "**System Rietz**" emerged. (Note that eventually System Rietz was also spelled System Reitz in England and the U.S.)

Max Rietz (1872-1956) studied at the Technische Hochschule in Karlsruhe. His first post after graduation was at the Dampfkesselfabrik Trenck (Trenck Boiler Factory). Later he became an independent engineer in Erfurt, his home town, and his areas of interest included construction of boilers and steam engines. Here, too, he was well known for his inventions. In 1952, on his eightieth birthday and in the fiftieth year of System Rietz, he was honored by Erfurt.

Within a few years System Rietz became accepted beyond the borders of Germany and was introduced in a wide range of slide rules by many important slide rule manufacturers – except for the American makers. Max Rietz had the same bad luck as all of the other inventors of further scales and scale combinations, namely that these advances could not be protected by German patent law because they were merely "instructions to the human mind." For this reason he received no royalties on any of the many slide rules that bore his name. Otherwise he might have become a very rich man.

Fig.20. A. Walther (1898-1967)

Another very widely produced scale arrangement, **System Darmstadt**, was developed in 1934 and was marketed about a year later. The creator of this scale arrangement was Dr. Alwin Walther (1898-1967), who was Professor and Director of the Institute for Practical Mathematics at the Technische Hochschule in Darmstadt. His lectures were adapted primarily to the practice of engineering, and mathematicians criticized him for "disclosing mathematics to engineers." He and his team carried the development of the System Rietz further, and the team's innovation was named after the city in which it was developed.

In order to use all the available space on the one-sided slide rule, the L scale (which was already available as part of System Rietz) was transferred to the upper beveled edge of the slide rule, and the S and T scales were transferred to the narrow lower edge. In addition, the Pythagorean scale P appeared below the D scale. The three positive exponential scales LL1, LL2, and LL3 replaced the S, T, and L scales on the back of the slide. This maximal use of space was necessary because the one-sided slide rule had become standard in Germany. With the introduction of wider plastic models such as the Aristo 967U and the Faber-Castell 111/54, System Darmstadt was expanded to include BI and ST scales.

System Darmstadt was introduced first by Faber-Castell in 1935. None of the scales in the Darmstadt format were new. However, just as with System Rietz, the System Darmstadt succeeded because the most useful scales were optimally arranged and were made available at the right time to the enormously increased market made up of engineers and technologists.

Meanwhile, in North America another development, **the double-sided or duplex slide rule**, was taking form. In 1891 William Cox (a mathematics consultant to Keuffel & Esser Co.) patented a revolutionary slide rule construction. This slide rule had scales on both the front and the back surfaces of the body and the slide. There was space enough to add the both LL scales and folded scales. Furthermore the double-faced cursor referred to all scales (both front and back) simultaneously. Keuffel & Esser, the first commercial maker of slide rules in the U.S., manufactured both Mannheim rules and Cox's new double-sided rule, but the double-sided rule lead K&E away from the elaboration of the single-sided rule that took place in Europe.

Until the introduction of the double-sided rule, European manufacturers concentrated their product lines on slide rules, of various sizes and construction, with System Rietz and System Darmstadt as well as special purpose slide rules.

Double-sided slide rules appeared in Europe in the early 1950s. They were known collectively as duplex rules. Most makers used expanded versions of this term, e.g., Duplex [46], Novo-Duplex (Faber-Castell), Rietz-Duplex, Multimath-Duplex, and Polymath-Duplex (Nestler). However, Dennert & Pape (Aristo) adopted an entirely new term ("Studio") for their very successful duplex.

The Japanese maker Hemmi also adopted System Rietz and System Darmstadt. Hemmi used the general term duplex for its double-sided slide rules. Meanwhile, in North America, as before, the simple scale arrangements carried the name "Polyphase-Mannheim Type."

However, in North America the slide rule offerings featured double-sided slide rules with names like Polyphase-Duplex-Trig, Polyphase-Duplex-Decitrig (i.e., decimal trig functions), Log Log Duplex Trig, Log Log Duplex Decitrig, Log Log Duplex Vector (all by Keuffel & Esser), and Maniphase Multiplex (by Dietzgen).

There were also such well-known scale systems as Electro, Disponent, Merchant, and Präzision (Precision). There were also slide rules such as the Tachymeter, machining-time, Stadia, and Stahlbeton (reinforced-concrete) with names that corresponded to their special fields of application. Finally, there were slide rules named after their inventors such as Yakota and Perry.

Important individual scales

The **reciprocal or inverse scale** is attributed to the Englishman Everard (1755). [47] It was later (1797) used and described by William Hyde Wollaston, but once again was forgotten. [48] The reciprocal scale was also attributed to Pearson, who wrote about a century later.

In the beginning the German makers designated reciprocal scales with the letter R. Later the letter designation I (for inverted) became the international standard. Eventually it became customary to link the reciprocal scale with the scale-pair C/D. The reciprocal scale was designated CI if it was installed on the slide or DI if it was installed on the stator. If the CI scale was folded on B, then the scale was designated CIF and appeared in the middle of the slide.

The **trigonometric scales** can be traced back to Edmund Gunter. However, only with the help of Amédée Mannheim, in the mid-1800s, did the trigonometric scales achieve an importance which led to applications in engineering and later to instruction in school. The classical trigonometric scales are the sine scale S and the tangent scale T (later designated T1). The S scale extended from

5° 43′ to 90°; the T1 scale extended from 5° 43′ to 45°. In the course of development, these two scales experienced several modifications in the way that they were coordinated with the basic (C/D) scales and in the way that the numerical value of the function was read.

Basically, until the mid-1900s these trigonometric scales were located in the upper or lower row on the back of the slide. Furthermore, until this same time, these scales were usually marked in degrees and minutes. (Systems Rietz and Mannheim were marked in degrees and minutes to the very end of their eras.) In the case of the classical Mannheim slide rule, the S and T scales ran in opposite directions. In order to read their numerical values, the slide was turned over and reinserted so that the S or the T scale was adjacent to the A scale. However, it became apparent that the numerical value of the T scale could be read more accurately from the D scale. For this reason, a few years later the T scale was changed to run from left to right. Thus, when the slide was turned over and reinserted, the S scale could be read off the A scale and the T scale could be read off the D scale. This arrangement of S and T scales prevailed up to the end of the slide rule era in Systems Rietz and Mannheim.

The slide (described above) was actually repositioned long after it was unnecessary. Around the beginning of the 1900s (Nestler in 1914 and D&P and Faber-Castell in the 1920s) small "slots" were milled in the back of the stator floor at the two ends and provided with index marks. [49] Now the user could move the slide so as to set the angle at the index mark on the back of the slide rule, turn the slide rule over, and read the numerical value off the A or D scales on the front.

As further refinements were introduced, the one-sided slide rule acquired a transparent index window in the floor of the stator, and a somewhat modified S scale was coordinated with the D scale. Thus, in the beginning the angle was set on the back of the slide rule; the slide rule was turned over and the numerical value was read off either the A scale or the D scale. Later both were read off the D scale. The ST scale for smaller angles and radian measurements (from 34′ to 5° 43′) also appeared about this time.

A decisive change followed after 1945, when the relocation of the S, T, and ST scales to the stator, their coordination with the D scale (pioneered in 1935 by System Darmstadt), and the introduction of decimal trig markings all gradually gained acceptance. This scale arrangement was very convenient and easy to understand, especially in the case of school slide rules. In addition to these changes, some models included a second T scale (from 45° to 84.5°) on the stator and a movable S scale on the slide.

Other odd and seldom-used variants were the SI and TI scales developed by Hemmi (before 1939). These co-functions ran right to left. They had red numbers or (less often) black numbers that were slanted to the left. Another example was the 400^g grade ("new degrees") format. However, this format only made sense in the case of Tachymetric models since this "new standard" (i.e., "grade" or "French decimal system") did not gain acceptance in other areas of specialization.

The English physician Peter M. Roget (1779-1869) is well known as the inventor of the **double-logarithmic or log-log** scale, which he called "logometric." He gained a name for himself through various activities and publications. [50] In 1814 he presented his invention of the log-log scales in a paper titled *Description of an Instrument for performing mechanically the involution and evolution of numbers*. (The paper was actually read before the Royal Society by Dr. Wollaston, who was already a member.) [see 48] This paper gained Roget membership in the Royal Society in 1815.

This was well-deserved since his log-log scales were a great advance toward the optimization of Gunter's idea. Roget's slide rule had a fixed double-logarithmic scale (1.25 to 10^{10}) on the upper part of the stator. On the slide there was a logarithmic scale (0.1-1-10), and on the lower stator there was second double logarithmic scale (1.0024 - 1.25). Roget recommended his slide rule for calculation of compound interest and calculation of probabilities. However, it was little-used and the log-log scale sank into obscurity until around the turn of the century when European and American makers took up the idea again. Typically there was a fixed log-log scale on the upper edges and lower edges of one-sided slide rules. The upper scale ran from 1.1 to 3.2 (later known as LL2); the lower scale ran from 2.5 to 10^5 (later known as LL3). However, other variations of the log-log scales were developed, the main reason being that these log-log slide rules found applications not only in the areas suggested by Roget but also in engineering mathematics.

As the first in a line of those who carried Roget's ideas further, we must mention the German engineer Blanc. As early as 1891 he proposed a slide rule that, for the first time, carried a positive log-log scale from 1.0015 to 10^6, a negative log-log scale from 0.00001 to 0.9985, as well as sin h and cos h. These scales were arranged on the slide. Two fixed A scales (1-100) were arranged on the stator above and below the slide. Blanc also used the symbol e as the characterisic base for the natural logarithms. Unfortunately his great idea could not be actualized. He was unable to find a slide rule maker that would produce his slide rule. According to Blanc, "the costs of production are not trivial and the range of applications is substantially narrower in comparison with the current conventional slide rule." Blanc's slide rule remained a noteworthy prototype. [51]

Other Englishmen, especially the mathematicians C. S. Jackson and J. Perry occupied themselves with log-log scales and made them better known in England. For example, a slide rule named after Perry was patented in England in 1901. The Perry slide rule was manufactured in England at the factory of the English firm A. G. Thornton, Ltd. The slide rule was also produced by Nestler in Germany, where it was designated "System Perry." Professor Perry's upper and lower scales ran from 1.1 to 10,000 and 0.93 to 0.0001 respectively. Thus the Perry slide rule included one negative LL scale.

A.W. Faber combined the LL2 and LL3 scales with a further step, i.e., the so-called Electro scales. In the first version (Model 378) of this series, the LL scales were located on the slanted lower edge of the stator and they were utilized by means of an index "tongue" or "tab" on the lower edge of the cursor. Later the LL scales were accommodated in the well of the stator. Eventually, these two LL scales were located in the top and bottom rows on the stator. This version of Model 378 was very successful and, with few changes, remained available through 1975. By that time both a wooden version (1/98) and a plastic version (111/98) were offered.

Dennert & Pape went their own way with the exponential slide rule called "System Schweth" (Model 297 beginning in 1902; Model 346 beginning in 1905). Schweth presented his slide rule at a meeting of scientists in Aachen in 1900, and F. Blanc raised objections to Schweth's claim that he was the first to publish on the subject of the exponential rule. These objections were indeed reasonable. Schweth argued against the claim that his slide rule carried additionally the scales seen in the standard slide rule of the time, which was then called the "multiplication slide rule." So Schweth's scales included A/B, C/D, plus a log-log scale from 1.2589 to 10 on the upper stator and a log-log scale from 10 to 10^{10} on the lower stator. [51]

Another significant development was the Yakota slide rule. Seinen Yakota (Jakota) was an assistant at the Imperial University in Tokyo. His slide rule had three positive and three negative log-log scales. He registered his invention (Patent No. 18218) in 1907 in England , and had it made by John Davis & Son, Ltd. Dennert & Pape produced a Yakota model in 1908.

Perhaps the requirements of slide rule users at that time did not match the Yakota. In any case his splendid idea could not retain a market. This is strange because obviously Yakota had developed an arrangement of six log-log scales which, 50 years later, would be the component of the immensely popular engineers' duplex slide rules.

In 1909 the American firm Keuffel & Esser introduced their log-log Duplex slide rule which had three positive exponential scales (designated LL1, LL2, and LL3) covering the range from 1.01 to 22,000. In 1924 the first supplementary LL0 scale appeared in a K&E product.

The Europeans had access to movable positive log-log scales rather late. Such scales appeared in 1935 in the System Darmstadt. Not until after World War II and the successful introduction of double-sided slide rules was it possible to accommodate six exponential scales in any European slide rule.

A further development stands out. In 1931 Hemmi was awarded a Japanese patent for a Guderman or G scale. Guderman (1798-1852) was a German mathematician who, among his other accomplishments, had occupied himself intensively with "The Theory of Exponential and Cyclic-hyperbolic Functions." This was the origin of the Hemmi log-log Model 153 Vector with patented G scales.

To bring this discussion about log-log scales to an end, I quote from the previously mentioned work of Rolf Jäger [52]:

> "There has been much experimentation with how the exponential scales are divided and arranged. In the end these scales were coordinated with the D scale, and the use of the base e made the convenient transition to natural logarithms possible."

Folded scales were described by Sylvanus Bevan [53] in 1817 in *Nicholson's Journal*. However, they were seldom incorporated in slide rules until 70 years later when, as already mentioned, Tscherepaschinski arranged a pair of scales folded at 3.16 along the lower slide-stator interface. Eventually folded scales became common, especially in American duplex slide rules, which had four slide-stator interfaces. Some early German models had scales that were folded at the square root of 10, but most folded scales were folded at the value of π. In general the scales folded at π were located along the upper slide-stator interface, and the C/D scales appeared on the same side in corresponding positions along the lower slide-stator interface. Thus the DF (folded D) scale appeared on the lower edge of the upper stator, and the CF scale appeared on the upper edge of the slide. Both scales began at the left with π, ran through 1, and ended on the right with π. The advantage of this arrangement was that, by using the DF/CF scales in conjunction with the C/D scales, the user could avoid the annoying need to reset the slide in order use the opposite index. Thus the linear slide rule acquired the same "endless scales" that were achieved with the circular slide rule. Furthermore the cursor hairline could be used with DF and D scales to multiply and divide by π directly. Some slide rules also acquired a CFI (inverted CF) scale in the middle of the slide. In the case of merchants' slide rules, the folded scales were folded at 3.6, thereby permitting direct multiplication or division by 360 days when carrying out calculations involving interest.

Another special feature was the so-called **"long"** or **"segmented"** scale. Theoretically the basic 1-10 scale could be extended to any desired length by dividing it into segments that would fit on the slide rule.

According to Cajori [54] the earliest segmented scale was proposed by Nicholson:

> "We refer to William Nicholson (1753-1815), well known as the editor of Nicholson's Journal. He prepared an article, in which different types of rules were described and the important problems taken up to increase the accuracy of the slide rule without increasing the dimensions of the instrument. According to his first design, a long logarithmic line was broken up in sections of convenient length and these placed parallel to each other on the face of the rule. Nicholson took ten such parallel lines, equivalent to a double line of numbers upwards to 20 feet in length."

However, this model did not work like a slide rule since there was no slide. Later on, Cajori [55] mentions J.D. Everett, Mannheim, Scherer (Scherer's Logarithmisch-graphische Rechentafel), and Hannyngton, all of whom designed slide rules with segmented scales side-by-side in the same plane. Hannyngton's extended slide rule had a long scale in sectional lengths fixed as a gridiron on a flat base, with a smaller slide in the same form. The scales had an effective scale length of 300 cm.

The French firm Tavernier-Gravet had already produced a 50 cm slide rule (designed by Ch. Lallemand) that had a 100 cm scale on both the stator and the slide. There was a fixed scale from 10-31 on the upper edge of the stator and a fixed scale from 32-100 on the lower edge of the stator. The slide carried a 1-31 scale on the lower edge and a 31-100 scale on the upper edge. In addition this slide rule had a small magnifying lens that could be rotated into position over the cursor.

Beginning in the early 1900s, models were being offered, under the designation "Präzision" (in Germany) and "Precision" (in England and the U.S.), which segmented the basic pair of one-cycle (1-10) scales and distributed the two segments along the upper and lower slide-stator interfaces. The upper segments ran from 1 to the square root of 10; the lower segments ran from the square root of 10 to 10. Sometimes models with scales segmented at 3.6 were available for business purposes (e.g., A.W. Faber's Columbus).

The most extreme example of a linear slide rule with segmented scales was the Hemmi-SUN-Super-Precision that "stretched" or extended the C, D, CF, and DF scales to a effective length of 240 cm. This slide rule is discussed in a later chapter. (See Fig. 52.)

Eventually this idea was picked up again by Faber-Castell and incorporated into the very successful Novo-Duplex. This slide rule had scale pairs which were segmented at the square root of 10 and were located on the back of the slide rule along the two slide-stator interfaces. Also Nestler eventually placed similar scales (R1 and R2) on the back of the stator in slide rule called the Multimath Duplex.

The advantage of this approach (i.e. the addition of segmented basic scales to a 25 cm duplex slide rule) was that the slide rule offered more precise basic calculations while also providing a complete set other of often-used scales such as the trigonometric scales and the log-log scales. [56]

The **Pythagorean scale** was designed by Parson in 1919 and was incorporated into a slide rule made in Japan. The Pythagorean scale became well known in Europe because of Walther's System Darmstadt. This scale was colored red and ran backwards from 0 to 0.995. The P scale was based on the Pythagorean Theorem and made it possible to read the sine and cosine of the smallest angles as well as the short side of a right triangle.

From 1912 through the 1920s, A.W. Faber had a **"System Hohenner"** and, upon request, equipped some standard slide rules with the Hohenner markings/divisions. This scale was linked to the value 8 on the D scale, was colored red, and ran from -20° on the left to +40° on the right. It was used in the calculation of barometrically measured differences in altitude.

The so-called **percentage scale** appeared on some merchants' or commercial models above the DF scale folded at 3.6. The percentage scale could be used to calculate rebates or surcharges.

So-called **extended markings** were added in the interest of ongoing improvement. Most one-sided linear slide rules, especially those that did not have folded scales, had the disadvantage that settings or readings could not be made to the left of 1 and to the right of 10. For that reason, slide rules with extended markings made use of the entire length of the slide rule by lengthening the scales to the left of 1 and to the right of 10. It is difficult to assign a date to this innovation; however, as a rule, extended markings were seen shortly after World War I on the most important models that were intended for engineers and technicians. Indeed, even special purpose models with this feature were offered. In some cases these short scale extensions were colored red. Actually this did not make sense since it was the convention to use red for all scales that ran from right to left (e.g., CI, CIF, DI, P, LL00, LL01, LL02, LL03) so that such scales could be recognized more easily. The same convention applied to the co-functions of sine and tangent which also ran from right to left.

Sometimes, instead of using red numbers, **slanted numbers** were used to call attention to a scale. For example, this was the case with K&E's Doric slide rules. This method was more economical since an additional imprint with red ink was not required.

The use of **background color** was noteworthy in the ongoing cavalcade of slide rule innovations and improvements. Typically background color was employed with only certain scales, usually those along the slide-stator interface. The use of background color actually began in the 1950s when the American firm Pickett & Eckel offered slide rules with yellow background. In this case, not only were the main scales colored, but the whole slide rule was colored "Eyesaver Yellow." The intent here was to provide sharpest "contrast" between markings and background in order to make it easier to read results. (In the case of the human eye, black markings on yellow background offer the sharpest contrast. [57]). Eventually the three main German makers followed the trend and offered certain models with background coloring. However, these firms scarcely mentioned the readability of individual markings and numbers. Instead these firms tended to use background color to emphasize whole scales or groups of scales. For example, Aristo provided yellow background for the movable scales along the slide-stator interface (e.g., B, CF, C). Faber-Castell did the same, but also provided green background for C/D scale-pair. In the case of the Novo-duplex, the A/B scale pair had a blue background. Certain Nestler models had slides with green background.

Gauge marks were extra marks added to scales to facilitate calculations involving constants. Some special-purpose slide rules had gauge marks for measurements of distance, for measurements of capacity, for molecular weight, etc. After 1900 it was common to add gauge marks to general purpose slide rules. Such marks included, for example:

π = 3.1416

C = $\sqrt{(4/\pi)}$ = 1.128   (Both C and C1 were used in calculating the

C1 = $\sqrt{(40/\pi)}$ = 3.57   area of a circle when given the diameter.)

M = $1/\pi$ = 0.318

σ = $\pi/180$ = 0.01745   (Used for small angles where arc $\alpha = \sigma \times \alpha$)

σ' = $180/\pi \times 60$ (Tangent sine arc in minutes)

σ'' =   (Tangent sine arc in seconds)

e = 2.71828   (The base for natural logarithms)

Merchants' or commercial models included gauge marks at 12 (for one dozen) and 144 (one gross).

Finally, **tables of constants** are worth mentioning. As early as the 1700s, such tables were added to some slide rules. The tables commonly included conversion factors for inches as well as factors for relating volume and weight of metals, oil, stone work, etc. An example of this was seen in Bevan's Engineer's slide rule (circa 1817). [58] In the case of single-sided slide rules of the 1900s, the tables were printed on paper strips and glued to the back of the stator. In the case of plastic slide rules, tables of constants were imprinted or applied using photochemical methods. Constants were provided that related to mathematics, mechanics, physics, electricity, power, work, strength, etc. Double-sided slide rules, which offered no space for such tables, were often furnished with tables printed on strips of cardboard or plastic. Like rulers, these strips might have had inch and cm scales along the edges. These strips were narrow and short enough to fit in the slide rule's case with the slide rule. In later years, such strips were also provided with one-sided slide rules.

The precision of settings and readings

For purposes of the following discussion, "precision" or "exactness" will mean how close the results obtained with the slide rule come to the results obtained by "long hand" calculation. In other words, how many significant digits can be obtained with the slide rule? Most slide rule users' guides, especially the leading guides published before 1950, deal with the exactness that can be obtained when reading a result. These guides also address whether this "attainable precision" or "exactness" is sufficient for most purposes. In the course of this century, the experience of technical engineers has confirmed the usual claims that most 10-inch slide rules are exact enough for practical purposes.

Karl Strubecker, Professor at the Technische Hochschule, Stuttgart, writes that "… the relative precision (h/x) of settings and readings along the main scales has the same constant value at all points along the scale, namely 0.5 % of the value x that being set or read. The value h/x is thus independent of whether one enters or reads a large or small number x." [59]

This can be confirmed by examining the C scale of a standard 10 inch slide rule (e.g., a K&E Log-Log Duplex Decitrig). At the left end of the scale the value 1.110 is marked, and the value 1.115 can be reliably interpolated. Thus the values 1.110 and 1.115 can be reliably distinguished. This is a relative precision of 0.005/1.110 = 0.005. In the middle of the scale where the intervals are the widest, the values 4.10 and 4.08 can be reliably distinguished. This is a relative precision of

0.02/4.10 = 0.005. Finally, at the right end of the scale the values 9.90 and 9.95 can be distinguished. This, too, is a relative precision of 0.05/9.90 = 0.005 or 0.5%.

In other words, settings and readings can be accurate to two decimal places on the basic C and D scales, 1% on the A scale, and 1.5% on the K scale. In practice, the important point is that the first two (or three) significant places can be set or read exactly on the usual 25 cm or 10 inch scale. The next digit (i.e., the third or fourth) is less precise. Of course, somewhat greater accuracy can be achieved with longer scales. The number of places that can be read by means of existing graduations is greater at the beginning of the scale (the "left end") than at the other end (the "right end").

It is also worth noting that errors that are made during settings and readings tend to average out during operations that involve several steps and slide settings. M. Hartmuth quotes an anonymous "competent mathematician" who is reported to have said about the slide rule, "Anyone who is troubled by questions of precision and significant digits, definitely does not understand the essence of the slide rule – at all!" [60]

It is worth mentioning that nearly all the renowned authors of slide rule books, the "pioneers," were engaged by the question of slide rule precision and accuracy. Over and over again, this issue gave contemporaries the impulse to innovate, and the resulting innovation (other than longer linear slide rules) resulted in the ability to read more significant digits accurately. Some of the innovations were mentioned in Nicholson's Journal, and Pickworth [61] described representative examples of such innovative devices as "Long Scale Slide Rules."

Cylindrical Slide Rules

The cylindrical slide rules (in German, Rechenwalzen) were the "ultimate" in long-scale slide rules. Large "desk models" were offered mainly by five makers:

1. Keuffel & Esser, U.S., made the **Thacher Rule** (US Patent No. 249117 granted 1881). This was on the market from around 1884 until 1950. It is estimated that around 6,000 Thachers were made. Three types are recognized [62, 63].

2. W. F. Stanley, England, made the **Fuller Slide Rule** (British patent No. 1044 granted 1878 and US patent No. 219246 granted 1878). It was on the market from 1875 until 1975. It is estimated that 14,000 Fullers were made. Four different types are recognized. [64]

3. A. Nestler AG, Germany, made the **Nestler Rechenwalze**. It was on the market from around 1922 until around 1937. The number of pieces made is not known. Three types are recognized. (Nestler catalog c. 1925).

4. H. Daemen-Schmid, Switzerland, made the **LOGA-Rechenwalze**. It was on the market from around 1900 to around 1935. More than 30,000 were made. Models in the following sizes are known: 1.2m, 2.4m, 7.5m, 10m, 15m, and 24m. [65]

5. J. Billeter, Switzerland, made the **Billeter - Rechenwalze**. [65]

The **Thacher rule** consists of a cylinder (4 inches in diameter and 18 inches long) that revolves in an open framework composed of twenty bars running lengthwise and held radially edgewise between two metal rings. The cylinder scale bears scales corresponding to the logarithmic scales of a standard linear slide rule 60 feet in length. These scales are duplicated on the exposed sides of the parallel bars. The number of "scale strips" or segments on the bars and cylinder total 40. The cylinder slides and rotates inside the framework and any part of any one of its scales can be set at any part of the scales on the bars. The cylinder is provided with a knob for sliding and rotating the cylinder. The framework bears a magnifier mounted on a bar, along which the magnifier can be moved as required. [66]

The whole instrument was made by Keuffel & Esser, but it is known that the plates for printing the scales were made by W.F. Stanley, London. This firm used a special dividing machine to engrave the scales for lithographic printing (i.e., on a stone). There were more than 30,000 strokes engraved on the plate. The dividing machine had an efficiency of a seven digit logarithmic table with an exactness of 0.0001 inch. It is known that at the time K&E was not able to divide slide rules. Therefore the scale must have been made by Stanley, leading to the inference that Stanley may have made the entire Thacher rule!

The Thacher Rule attains an exactness of reading nearly as precise as a five digit logarithmic table, i.e., approximately 1 to 20,000. Experts such as Thompson and Hammer [67] classified the Thacher as superior, easy to handle, and very fast. While the three types of Thachers differ in certain structural details, they are the same as to size and scales. [68]

The **Fuller slide rule** consists of a hollow outer cylinder that slides and rotates on an inner cylinder, which is provided with a handle. A single logarithmic scale nearly 42 feet long is wound helically on the outer cylinder and there are three indexes, one of which is located on a fixed pointer attached to the handle. A brass tube slides inside the cylinder and attached to it is a brass strip or bar parallel to the axis. The bar carries two indexes whose distance apart is the axial length of the helical scale, as well as a scale of equal parts for finding logarithms. On the cylinder are also printed a number of tables, gauge points, and settings. [69] The exactness of reading is approximately 1 to 10,000. The scales are imprinted with 7200 strokes. [67]

The four types of Fullers differ in structural details and in supplementary trig and log scales. [62, 63] They are not easy to operate, and therefore were not well regarded by some experts.

The **Nestler-Cylindrical Calculator (Rechenwalze)** can be compared with the Thacher Rule. There is a rotating cylinder with the "long scales." The slide consists of bars kept by two rings. The slide can rotate around the cylinder and move longitudinally along the cylinder. The clips or rings to hold the cylinder or the side bars carries clearly-marked intermediate values.

The three models differed in dimensions as follows:

Model	Length (inches)	Diameter (inches)	Scale Length (feet – inches)
2050	10	2.25	5 – 3
2051	13	3.5	12 – 3.5
2052	21	6.25	41 – 0

The **Loga-Rechenwalze** is very similar in design to the Thacher and Nestler. In all fairness it should be noted that the Nestler followed the Loga, which was protected by various patents awarded from 1907 through 1923.

All the cylindrical slide rules mentioned above were essentially large, "desk top" devices. There were also a few small "pocket-size" cylindrical rules. The best-known of these pocket cylinders is the **Otis-King calculator**. These are cylindrical devices with concentric, telescoping cylinders. On the surface of each cylinder is a continuous, spiral logarithmic scale. The telescoping parts can be turned, and calculations are carried out by sliding and rotating the cylinders relative to each other. The length is 6 inches when collapsed and 10 inches when fully extended; the diameter is 1.25 inches; the effective scale length is 42 inches. The Otis-King was manufactured from around 1923 to 1972 in various models and types. Types differed in minor structural variations over time. Models differed as to their scales. [70]

Slide Rule Makers and Their Models

This chapter discusses the most important slide rule makers, their history, and their development from the mid-1800s until the end of the slide rule era. Makers from several countries are mentioned. The decision to include a particular maker in this section was influenced by the status of the brand name, by the volume of slide rules produced, and by distribution outside the country of origin. In each case, the reader is provided with the firm's name at the time that it began, the names which were adopted later, and the brand names. For some important firms, the reader will find a list of the whole range of slide rules offered by the firm. [71]

England

Although England was the birthplace of the slide rule, only a few English slide rule makers survived to 1975. Clearly before the mass production of slide rules there were many slide rule makers operating out of little workshops. For example, there exists a list of over 300 slide rule makers before 1900, and names like W.F. Stanley, J. Rathbone & Sons, Fowler & Co., John Davies & Co., L.P. Casell, Fearnes, R.F. Agnew were well-known. However, only three remained significant producers through the mid-1970s, and only these three companies will be discussed below.

Blundell Brothers, Ltd   **BLUNDELL**

W. H. Harling, London   **W. H. HARLING**

Blundell Harling, Ltd. Weymouth   **BLUNDELL**

HARLING

The firm called **Blundell** has operated as a dye-works and felt maker since 1851 in Luton, England. Blundell only became involved with the manufacture and distribution of high quality slide rules, rulers, and drawing instruments after World War II when the company realized that it needed to develop other uses for its machine shop, and the manufacture of slide rules was suited to the machinery that was available. [73]

In 1964 Blundell acquired the firm W. H. Harling, and since 1968 the combined firm has been called Blundell Harling, Ltd.

Harling, when acquired, was already a well-known brand name with a long-established product line. At first Harling offered slide rules made by A.W. Faber, K&E, and Nestler. In 1900 Harling started making and selling its own slide rules, including models 702, 704, 706, and 708. These rules were made of mahogany and had celluloid scales A/B, C/D plus L, S, T. The various models differed in minor ways. Model 708 also had a log-log scale.

After the two firms merged, the manufacture of slide rules remained in the hands of the Blundell division, while Harling specialized in drawing instruments. The last line of Blundell Harling slide rules was the 0428 series, including the Basic, the LogLogtrig, the Rietz, the Navigational, and the Simplified Rietz, all 25 cm plastic slide rules. A 12.5 cm Simplified Rietz was also available, as well as some special purpose rules, e.g., the Mk6A Humidity (Model 0420.00), the Pilot Balloon (0420.50), the PG.54 Photographic Interpretation (420.70), and the Radar Wind (0420.60). These all had 25 cm scales, and the double-sided models had very distinctive stator bars. Blundell Harling continued to offer these special-purpose slide rules into the 1980s.

A.G. Thornton Ltd., Manchester   THORNTON P.I.C.

This firm was founded in 1878 by Alexander George Thornton in partnership with J. Halden. Thornton had been trained by Harling. In 1890 he established his own independent workshop and adjoining sales office in Manchester. By 1895 he had a constantly expanding factory for the manufacture of first-rate drawing instruments and (from c. 1904) slide rules, a large proportion of which were exported. By 1915 the Thornton line was described as the "largest and broadest in the United Kingdom." A catalog from the 1930s lists more than 70 different models carrying the P.I.C. brand name. (The **P**recision **I**nstrument **C**ompany had been taken over by Thornton in 1900.) Most of these slide rules had the scales for basic calculations. The line included one model (the Reitz) with System Rietz. (By now System Rietz was an established designation, something that Rietz himself wanted to avoid. However, this practice was already firmly established among other English makers.) The majority of P.I.C. slide rule models were of high quality. They were made of mahogany and had framed-glass cursors and springy stator floors. Of course, after 1960 models made of plastic were included in the product line. In 1960 the firm was renamed British Thornton; in 1980 it was sold by the founders' successors and began producing office furniture. The firm was liquidated in 1992. [74]

The Unique Instrument Co., Brighton   UNIQUE

This company was founded around 1922 by Burns Snodgrass. At the time a lecturer at the Brighton Technical College, he had made some practice slide rules for a colleague who gave them to his students. A year later Snodgrass made his first delivery of hand-made slide rules to a wholesaler. In the following years the product line was expanded to include drawing instruments, and Snodgrass undertook distribution of his own products. In 1935 Unique exhibited at trade shows for the first time. Until 1945 the rather small workforce, working in a very modern factory, produced 100,000 pieces per year. After World War II Burns' son Henry C. Snodgrass joined the firm, took over the technical production, and also concerned himself with exports.

At that time the slide rule offerings included a U-series (consisting of four "Universal" models), two log-log rules, two "Legible"-G (with markings that were more widely spaced and thicker, to make them easier to read), two Precision (10/20 and 5/10), a "Commercial" (C), an "Electrical" (E), and a Navigation (N). In addition there was the D1-D3 "Dualistic," a patented innovation, with duplicate C and D scales for "faster calculating" and expanded log-log scales. The M1 "Monetary" slide rule had only C and D scales plus a table of English exchange rates on the upper edge. Last, but not least, there was a "Brighton Rule," that corresponded exactly to the German System Darmstadt.

Snodgrass made some interesting comments about the Brighton [75], stating "Another kind of difficulty sometimes facing the producer is to satisfy the requirements of the overseas purchasing organizations in respect of the arrangement of scales on the slide rule." He went on to complain that such special requests complicated the product line and hampered production. Later he noted that "The Brighton slide rule was designed to meet the requirements of one of the Continental countries whose purchasing agent demanded a specific arrangement of scales. There is nothing which makes it more suitable for one country than for any other." [75] Snodgrass spoke of the "scale equipment" on the Brighton as very extensive and went on to describe the scales of the System Darmstadt. Undoubtedly he was forced to take into consideration how well-known the System Darmstadt was and chose the name "Brighton" for his version of the same slide rule.

The above description of the development of the "Brighton" models, and the other slide rules in the Unique product line, is interesting because Burns Snodgrass was, without a doubt, extremely creative and original. For example, one distinctive feature of Unique slide rules was the "long" slide. In various models, the slide was so long that it protruded at all times from one end or the other of the stator. This made the slide easier to grasp and operate.

It was the Snodgrass' marketing strategy to underbid all his competitors substantially. For this reason Unique slide rules were very inexpensive, but of lower quality. (They were usually made of lower quality boxwood.) The scales were produced in a special way, transferred to narrow, transparent celluloid strips that were, in turn, glued to white background strips and then attached to the stator and slide with metal pegs or brads. Unique experienced a steady increase in sales until production of slide rules was discontinued in 1975. [76]

Germany

Ausschuß für wirtschaftliche Fertigung, Berlin   AWF
(includes Arbeitsgemeinschaft für Rechentechnik)   (ART)

AWF stands for Ausschuß für wirtschaftliche Fertigung (roughly "the Commission for Efficient Production"). This Commission was founded in 1918 "…to encourage team-work and the creation of the basis for the communication of the latest knowledge and experience relating to production efficiency."

The Commission and its various sub-committees worked on a multitude of practical problems and their solutions. The "by-products" of `this activity were "aids" such as graticles, half-ray boards, calculating boards, data slides and the AWF special slide rules, on which the Committee for Calculating Technology worked very hard and very successfully. The first model of an AWF-special slide rule appeared in the early 1930s, and a table from 1952 (83) shows the development of forty versions for uses in various fields. These versions were numbered AWF 701 (machine time), AWF 702 (belt power and velocity), and so on through 749. (A few numbers remain unassigned.) In addition AWF offered blank versions of the slide rule (with one or two slides) for the fussy person who wanted to inscribe his own settings. There were versions of this slide rule for such unusual fields as radio cross-talk suppression, blended heating gas operation, drying artificial wood, weavers' loom and loom-group utilization, and many others. The devices were constructed with one or two slides and printed scales encased in Cellophane, in accordance with patents obtained by Dr. Ing. Seehase (DRP 394337 in 1924; 729162 in 1942; and 747007 in 1944). [also 83]

Dennert & Pape, Altona	**Dennert & Pape**
	D&P
	DUPA
ARISTO-Werke Dennert & Pape KG, Hamburg	**ARISTO**

This firm was founded in 1862 by J.C. Dennert. Martin Pape became a partner around 1863. Dennert had initially taken over the workshop of Carl Plath (who subsequently formed his own company to make nautical instruments). The firm, at that point, manufactured theodolytes, transits, other geodetic instruments, drafting scales, drafting instruments and planimeters. During this period, most slide rules were imported from France, but the flow of slide rules from France encountered difficulties during and after the Franco-Prussian War (1870-71).

For that reason, the master builder A. Goering (1841-1906) of Halberstadt (later Professor at the Technische Hochschule in Berlin) encouraged Dennert & Pape to take on the manufacture of slide rules, a task for which D&P was

Fig.21. J.C. Dennert (1829 - 1920)

especially well suited. D&P, in collaboration with Goering, established a scale arrangement that was better than those seen in the imported French models, and Goering wrote a users' guide. This first D&P slide rule appeared on the market in 1872. It was made of boxwood with blackened scales and had scales A/B and C/D, as well as a cursor similar to the one developed by Amádée Mannheim.

In 1886 D&P introduced a substantial structural improvement in the form of white celluloid scales. An important German patent was obtained for that improvement. The title of the patent was "The Unchangeable Ruler" (Unveränderlicher Maßstab). A celluloid veneer was fixed to the stator and the slide in order to preclude the linear expansion of the wood. However, most importantly, this innovation, through the contrast of the black scales on the white background, substantially improved the readability of the scales. In 1888, after this new technique had proved itself useful for rulers, it was also applied to slide rules. As a result, a layer of celluloid was affixed to mahogany. The new precision of the markings and the improved readability of the scales set a standard for all new rulers, and gradually other makers copied this construction.

The steadily growing demand for slide rules, plus the design and development of the necessary dividing machines (which were also exported) required the construction of a new factory. This was completed in 1900. For its time, the factory had very modern equipment, with electrically driven machines and a workshop for making precision instruments. In addition to the production of slide rules, there was an emphasis on the fabrication of precision instruments and optical instruments.

In the long run, D&P developed a wide assortment of slide rules for various applications. During this process the "slide action," the cursor, and the materials used for slide rules were all improved.

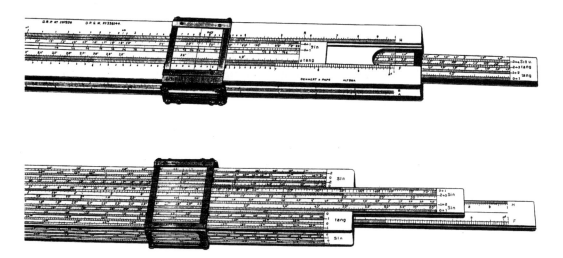

Fig.22. Celestial navigation slide rule by Nelting

Of the many D&P slide rules made around 1900 one in particular should be mentioned, i.e., the Nautical Astronomical and Universal Slide Rule with System Nelting. At the time (c. 1912), this slide rule cost the staggering price of 140 Marks, which would be twice the monthly earnings of a harbor worker in Hamburg. Understandably few of these slide rules have found their way into the hands of collectors.

Robert Nelting registered his slide rule for a patent, and the Imperial Patent Office granted him patent No. 207234 in 1907. At first he attempted to be an independent distributor of his slide rule. However, eventually D&P succeeded in acquiring the distribution rights for the Nelting and made it part of the D&P product line.

The following description of the Nelting is abstracted from the users' guide:

> "The Nautical Astronomical and Universal Slide Rule is like a logarithmic and astronomical table of unlimited scope and is more complete than anything else like it. It can be used for general mathematical problems and for all nautical calculations with the precision required for navigation. The slide rule includes scales for simple multiplication and division, for square root, for cube root, for the trigonometric functions sine, tangent, cosine, and cotangent, as well as their roots and squares, plus scales for the reciprocals. The trigonometric functions are expressed in time as well as arc. In addition, the scales permit direct conversion of degrees to compass points, of time to arc, and vice versa. Calculations can be carried out using time, degrees, or compass points directly."

The users' guide goes on to say, " The slide rule embodies the whole of mathematics."

This is truly a bold claim. Nevertheless, it describes a very interesting slide rule that could be the source of great pleasure for a specialist or collector. Even the users' guide itself is fascinating reading. The slide rule is a beautifully made, technical masterpiece. There are two slides, one on each side of the stator. The partition between them has windows and indexes for reading the scales on the back (or inner) side of each slide.(See Figure 22.)

Even before World War I, D&P had a wide-ranging line of both standard engineering slide rules and special purpose slide rules. At first they were made of boxwood, then boxwood laminated with celluloid scales, and later mahogany with celluloid scales.

By 1936. a pivotal year for D&P, the firm had offered over 250 different models of various construction and with various scale arrangements. Among them was the DUFIX, a double-sided slide rule with scales K, A/ST, BI/D, L on the front and DF/CF, CIF, C/D on the back.

In addition, there were three models of the Präzision with "segmented scales" that effectively doubled the exactness of reading. There were also special purpose slide rules: the "Shipboard Cargo and Navigation Officer's slide rule"; a slide rule for making insurance calculations; slide rules for premiums and net reserve; the Tachymetry slide rule; the Schweizer Topograph; the Material Testing slide rule (System Weißkopf); the Special Slide Rule for Machining Speeds, Travel, Runtime, etc. (System Kresta); Universal Surveying and Topography Slide Rule; Reinforced Concrete; Behrens' Pipeline Construction Slide Rule; Behrens' "Colorator" for Heat and Cold Transmission Calculations; and the Drainage/Sewer Slide Rule (System Vikari). The slide rules for students included the "Simzet" and the "Riezet."

In 1936, Georg Dennert decided to discontinue the production of wooden slide rules, and the era of the very successful all-plastic slide rule began under the brand name ARISTO. (The name was derived from the impact-resistant PVC polymer ASTRALON that was available at that time.) The production of slide rules, which until that time had involved much hand finishing, was converted to a more industrial process. Special equipment was obtained, some of which was developed "in house." Not surprisingly, the new product line was restricted at first. Only those scale systems in great demand remained, and a new system for numbering models was introduced. The initial line of ARISTO slide rules included models 92 (Normal), 99 (Rietz), 914 (Electro), 943 (Merchant's), and, around 1940, the 967 (Darmstadt).

During World War II the factory in Altona survived the heavy bombing of Hamburg relatively well, and by 1945 production of slide rules had resumed. At this time D&P devoted considerable attention to the double-sided slide rule and the "American" scale system. This bold move succeeded. Out of it came the very successful Aristo-Scholar for the student and the Aristo-Studio for the engineer.

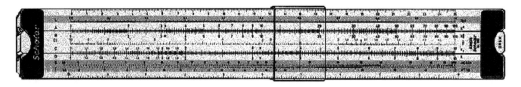

Fig.23. The Aristo-Scholar slide rule of 1949

The Aristo-Scholar appeared around 1949 and was, for students, a genuine innovation. In addition to this slide rule's recognized quality and ease of use, the Aristo-Scholar offered an advantage that was missing from the previous "school Rietz." Like the prototype of the Darmstadt, the S and T scales on the Aristo-Scholar were located directly under the D scale on the lower stator. This made it easy to quickly "look up" or read the values for these functions. Later (around 1956) the ST scale was added to permit settings and readings involving angles as small as 0.55° - 6°. The fractions of degrees were now expressed in decimal fractions instead of minutes and seconds, as seen in systems Mannheim and Rietz.

During subsequent years, expanded scale systems were introduced. These slide rules, with the new systems, carried such names as Scholar LL, Scholar VS2, Bischolar, Bischolar II, and Trilog. These school models gained leadership in the German market and became world-known. The same was true for the Aristo-Studio.

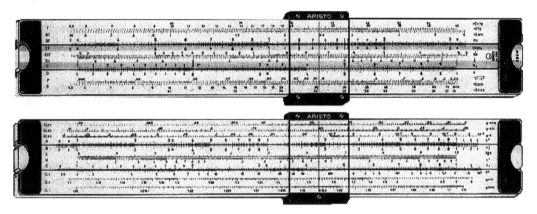

Fig.24. The Aristo-Studio slide rule of 1949

The Aristo Studio was virtually perfect! It was two-sided with stator bars at the ends and a "wrap-around" cursor. This construction made it possible to incorporate the 23 most important scales and to arrange them in the ideal relationship to each other. Actually the Aristo-Studio was a hybrid of the Rietz and the Darmstadt systems. It had scales folded at π, positive exponential scales (per System Darmstadt), and even negative exponential scales. These were all arranged in a very clever way that suited the needs of the practicing engineer. For the European user at that time, the Aristo-Studio was a bit of a sensation, especially since the American and Japanese double-sided slide rules were not yet widely known in Europe. (The few prewar German double-sided slide rules made by Nestler and D&P did not establish themselves, and these wooden slide rules were not offered after 1945 since they had essentially become obsolete.) The Aristo-Studio was available in

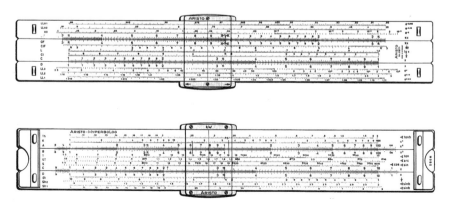

Fig 25. The Aristo-Hyperbolog ("Vector") slide rule – front and back

12.5 cm, 25 cm and 50 cm lengths. In addition there was a 25 cm model with the 400^g "New Degrees" markings. By 1970, more versions of the Studio had followed: the Aristo-Studiolog (12.5 cm and 25 cm); the Multilog (12.5 cm, 25 cm, 50 cm), and the Hyperlog (25 cm). There were also the following Aristo rules: the Electro Special, the Attenuation (Wave Dampening) slide rule, the Textile slide rule (System Beck), the Geodetic slide rule, and three Reinforced Concrete slide rules (for n=10, n=15, and n = any value).

Of course, in addition to the new double-sided slide rules, the tried-and-true one-sided slide rules were also offered. Models Darmstadt, Electro, and Commerce II had an especially elegant and functional design. The stator had a continuous layer of transparent plexiglass with index marks (hair lines) which made it possible to read and set values on the back of the slide.

Also, some very exceptional devices t hat were based on slide rules deserve mention. The Aristo-Naviat was designed for nautical use by "weekend and long-distance sailors." The Aristo-Aviat was designed for the private and professional pilot and was available in several versions. The Aristo-AviatJet had a scale for speed that extended to Mach 3.5. Aristo was the only maker of such rules in Europe, and they were very much liked by their users. These models are occasionally sold and used to this day.

Bayerische Reißzeugfabrik, Nürnberg   ECOBRA
(Bavarian Drafting Instrument Factory, Nürnberg)

This firm is among those who started producing slide rules more recently. The firm was founded in 1893 under the name Eichmüller & Co. The factory made drafting compasses and grew steadily, in part due to sales to the major American importer Eugene Dietzgen & Co. Partner Joseph Dietzgen acquired the factory in 1909 after the death of Eichmüller. In 1922 the name was changed to Bayerische Reißzeugfabrik (Bavarian Drafting Instrument Factory, Inc.)

The company began to make slide rules just before World War II under the brand name ECOBRA, derived from **E**ichmüller & **Co**.-**B**ayerische **R**eißzeugfabrik **A**G. Here again, Eugene Dietzgen was its main customer. ECOBRA slide rules were also sold, in modest numbers, in Europe.

The manufacture of ECOBRA slide rules began with a stock made of aluminum alloy. The scales were etched in and then colored black. Initially there were three pocket models (1250, 1160, and 1460 (Rietz)) and three 25 cm models (1300, 1500/3 (Rietz), and 1600 (Elektro)). After 1950 an improved alloy was introduced. The "blank" stock was sprayed with white enamel, the scale system was printed on the slide rule, and, finally, a protective coat of lacquer was applied.

The last models (12.5 and 25.cm) offered by the company combined System Rietz, System Darmstadt, and the Elektro. The resulting versatile, double-sided, slide rule was called the COSMOS.

ECOBRA was one of the few slide rule makers to produce metal slide rules. However, the advantage of the unparalleled stability of such slide rules was offset by the increased weight and the reduced "slide action," which was attributable to the metal-on-metal slide-stator interface. Also, the preferences of slide rule users trended toward wood or pure-white plastic. Metal slide rules, at least in Europe, did not gain a large share of the market.

After the end of the slide rule era, ECOBRA continued to offer writing drafting tools and writing instruments.

A.W. Faber-Castell

Fabrik für Rechenschieber

A.W. Faber – Geroldsgrün

A.W. Faber-Castell GmbH & Co., Stein

A. W. FABER

A.W. FABER-CASTELL

FABER-CASTELL

1861 was the 100-year jubilee of the world famous Faber pencil factory in Stein near Nürnberg. It was also the year that the factory in Geroldsgrün was founded in 1861 by Baron Lothar von Faber, an important entrepreneur of his time. The factory at Geroldsgrün was established to make slates, rulers, measuring sticks, drafting triangles, and T-squares. Since Faber already had the technology for making precise, high-value rulers, the addition of slide rules to the Faber product-line was an obvious next step.

Fig.26. Lothar Frh. v. Faber (1817-1896)

The first Faber slide rules appeared in 1892. Made of boxwood, most had the Mannheim scale arrangement that was usual at that time. While these slide rules were first offered in Germany, they were soon available, through the firm's own branch offices, in England, France, and the U.S.

Until approximately 1924, the Faber-Castell slide rules were made of boxwood. This was followed by a transition to slide rules made of mahogany (50 cm) and then pearwood. In rapid

Fabrik für Lineale, Massstäbe, Winkel, Reisschienen u. s. w.
von A. W. FABER in Geroldsgrün.

Fig.27. View of Faber factory around 1900

succession, scales of celluloid veneer were adopted, and the framed cursor with glass window and hairline was developed.

Like other slide rule makers, Faber took pains to make structural improvements in the slide rule. For example, A.W. Faber obtained several patents for the stabilization of the slide and stator, plus others for the stator with a spring in the floor. The 1912-1913 Faber catalog shows 12 slide rules from the so-called "300 series." The earliest of these rules had no model numbers. They were followed by the Mannheim model 350 (which was initially made of boxwood and later of boxwood with celluloid facings.) Also included in the catalog were Model 361 (with scales A/B, C/D) for trade schools; Model 360 (with the additional S, T, and L scales on the back of the slide); Model 380 (the 50 cm version of Model 360); and Model 367 (with special digit-registering cursor).

There were two other early Faber slide rules of special interest: "System Pickworth" and "System Schumacher." "System Pickworth" was developed by Faber in collaboration with the Englishman Charles N. Pickworth, who had already established a reputation through his books on slide rules. In 1894 Pickworth published the book *The Slide Rule: A Practical Manual* [77] that went through several editions. He also wrote a special guide for Faber-Castell slide rules initially called *Instructions for the Use of A.W. Faber's Calculating Rule.* The book first appeared around 1897 and went through several editions and versions before WWI.

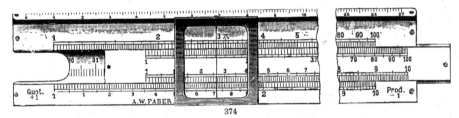

Fig.28. A.W. Faber's "Pickworth" slide rule

"System Pickworth" appeared in two Faber slide rules, Model 374 (with 25 cm scales) and Model 384 (with 50 cm scales). In addition to the usual scales (A/B, C/D-S, L, T), these slide rules had a characteristic and peculiar arrangement of the K scale, which was read through a window that was routed out of the back of the stator. (See Figure 11.)

"System Schumacher" appeared on a one-sided, wooden slide rule (Model 366) with divisions at equal intervals. The markings were based on a number of theoretical indices.

Neither "System Pickworth" nor "System Schumacher" gained acceptance. "System Pickworth" was soon replaced by improved models (especially the Electro and the Rietz); "System Schumacher" was difficult to understand and poorly suited for rapid calculation.

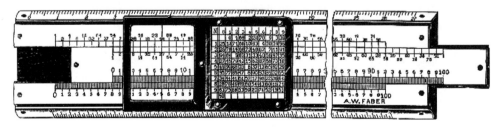

Fig.29. A.W. Faber's "Schumacher" slide rule

In 1905 the firm's name was changed from A.W. Faber to A.W. Faber-Castell.[78] However, in the case of slide rules, until about 1913 the trademark remained a stylized balance scale marked A.W. Faber. This was replaced by A.W. FABER followed by two framed towers which lay horizontal and bracketed the word CASTELL. After 1930, A. W. FABER appeared only on simple slide rules for beginners. After 1950 the word CASTELL appeared on the left end of the slide.

By the 1930s, Faber-Castell was already offering 44 different slide rule models, all designated with model numbers in the "300 series." The eleven, low-priced school models comprised the majority of the slide rules that were sold. However, various special purpose slide rules were made in response to suggestions from outside experts. For example, Model 348, "System Dr. Winkel," was designed for determining the run-times for all operations involving machining, turning, and boring. Although the model designation changed [79], "System Dr. Winkel" was retained (with modifications) through 1972.

Other special purpose slide rules included a slide rule for forestry officers, one for lumber dealers, two versions of "System Hohenner" (for the barometric determination of altitude differences), and, last but not least, the "Columbus." This slide rule (Model 342) was designed by Albert Rohrberg for use by merchants. It came with a special instruction book of its own. Indeed, Rohrberg was, as already mentioned, one of the significant experts who spoke out for the wider use of slide

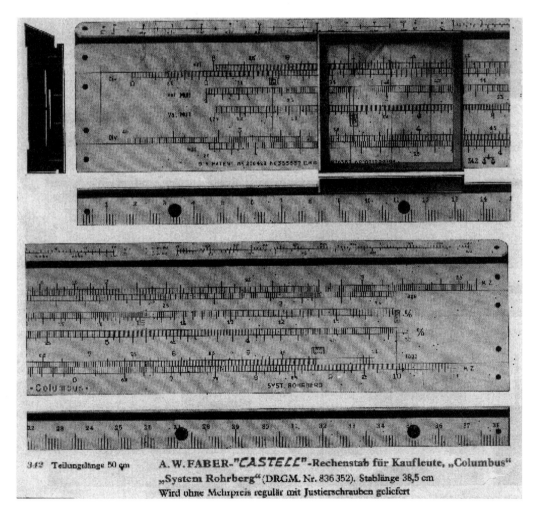

Fig.30. A.W. Faber-Castell's "Columbus" slide rule

rules, especially slide rules for merchants. Moreover, Faber-Castell was successful in winning Rohrberg as an ally. In spite of the requisite neutrality of his lectures, Rohrberg always used CASTELL slide rules and demonstration models. He drew on his experience to offer many useful suggestions for improving rules.

It should be mentioned here that, for its time (c. 1925), the "Columbus" had a very interesting and well-thought-out scale system for commercial calculations. There were short-lived versions (Models 310 and 320 had 12.5 cm scales; Models 307 and 327 had 25 cm scales) for the business student. These simple rules had only three scales and were later replaced by Model 342 (designated 3/42) for the professional merchant.

The "Professional Model" (342) was offered "for great accuracy when used for multiplication, calculation of per cent, calculation of discounts and markups, also the most complicated forms of interest calculation based on 360 and 365 days, size and weight conversions, arbitrage, rule-of-three (i.e., rule of proportion) calculations, chain-rule calculations, statistics, and the adjustment of price tables."

Thus, the "Columbus" offered everything that a merchant could wish for. In spite of this, it could not compete beyond the end of the 1930s. Its large size and unorthodox scale arrangement were to blame for this. The "Columbus" was made of pearwood and, briefly, of ebony. The stock was 38.5 cm long, and the scales were 25 cm long, excluding extensions. On the two slide-stator interfaces. the Columbus had a pair of extended scales. The scales along the upper slide-stator interface began at 0.8 and ran through 1.0 to 3.6. The scales along the lower slide-stator interface began at 2.5 and ran through 10 to 12.5 (or 1.25). These two sets of scales were displaced, or "folded," at 3.16 units, i.e., the square root of 10. Along the middle of the slide there were two coordinated reciprocal (inverted) scales. One ran from 1 to 4; the other from 3.1 through 10, with an extension to 12.5).

By the way, there was an interesting and practical "fixed scale pair" on the slanted upper edge of the stator next to two conversion scales for English money. With this fixed scale pair, one could convert percent of purchase price directly to percent of selling price and vice versa. This is a task that still causes problems today – even for people with access to pocket calculators. This little "wonder scale" never achieved the recognition that it deserved, although it appeared again later on certain merchant slide rules.

The most popular slide rule in the 300 series was the "Standard" (Model 360), with scale configuration A/B, C/D-S, L, T (known in the U.S. as the Mannheim type). The next most popular slide rule was the "Slide Rule for Electrical and Mechanical Engineers" (Model 378). System Rietz gained in popularity until the early 1930s.

Like other German slide rule makers, A.W. Faber-Castell continued to develop and refine the concept of the one-sided slide rule. Of course there were also efforts (reflected in three patents obtained after 1933) to construct a double-sided slide rule. However, as surviving test models demonstrate, the efforts to develop the double-sided slide rule (with its potential for a substantially larger set of scales) were half-hearted, and the project was eventually dropped.

The well-established System Rietz and the Elektro were followed, in 1935, by Professor Alwin Walther's System Darmstadt. The Darmstadt was available in three sizes (12.5, 25 and 50 cm) and, next to the System Rietz, was one of the most popular technical slide rules sold. Note that the System Darmstadt was marketed first by Faber-Castell, and this resulted in a substantial increase in business for Faber-Castell in the 1930s.

In 1935 the "300 series" was replaced by a new system of model numbers. The result was a confusing multitude of "transition" model numbers which incorporated the old and new model numbers. For example, the famous Elektro (formerly Model 378) became Model 1/78/378 and later 1/78. Thus wooden slide rules with 25 cm scales acquired the designator "1/" followed by a two digit number based on the previous model number. The 25 cm version of System Rietz (formerly Model 387) became Model 1/87/387 and later Model 1/87. The designator "4/" indicated models with 50 cm scales. Initally designators "61/" and "63/" were used for slide rules with 12.5 cm scales. At that time these rules were made either entirely of celluloid or of wood with celluloid scales. Later the designator "67/" was used for 12.5 cm rules made of injection molded PVC. Finally, special purpose slide rules of wood belonged to a series of their own designated "3/".

Before World War II, A.W. Faber-Castell was the only company to offer a combination of the slide rule and the adding machine, which obviated the need to carry out addition and subtraction by hand or in an awkward way on the slide rule. The **"Addiator"** was the idea of Carl Kübler, who received a patent for it in 1937 (DRP 655353).

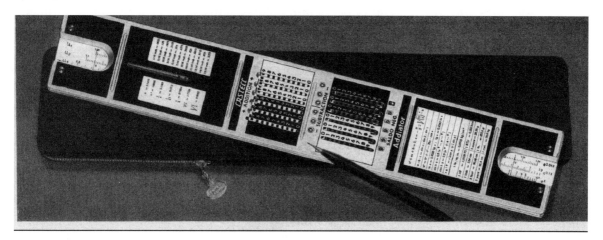

Fig.31. Faber-Castell slide rule with Addiator

The slide rule offered Kübler yet another place to market his Addiator. The so-called Addiator "cassettes" were obtained from the C. Kübler Additator Calculating Machine Company in Berlin and fastened to the back of the slide rule stator. The Addiators were usually made of brass, but during the shortages that followed World War II, some were made of sheet metal. In the case of wooden slide rules, the Addiator was inserted in the body of the slide rule and held in place by an Astralon plate which was fixed in place by screws. In the case of plastic slide rules, the Addiator was slipped into two lateral slots and then screwed in place.

Around 1954-55, in accordance with DBP 1062040, there was an attempt to make the Addiator casing of injection molded plastic and to rivet the Addiator casing and the plastic stator together. This led to defects and complaints and had to be abandoned. From then on, the light metal Addiator cassette was installed in two lateral slots and screwed in place.

The following slide rule/Addiator combinations were available: System Rietz, System Darmstadt, the Disponent (all 25 and 12.5 cm), the Normal, the Normal-Trig, and the Elektro (12.5 cm only). The slide rules of standard length (25 cm) with Addiator carried the suffix "-A." The shorter slide rules (12.5 cm) with Addiator carried the suffix "-R." Thus, for example, the 25 cm wooden System Rietz was designated Model 1/87A. Model 63/87R was celluloid with wooded core. Model 111/87A was a plastic slide rule with 25 cm scales.

The Faber-Castell factory at Geroldsgrün suffered no damage during World War II. Naturally during the war and the years immediately after the war there were shortages of materials and labor. However, in 1946 production was resumed with a cadre of experienced engineers and workers. The first slide rules to be made had the proven and well-known scale systems and were made of wood only or, in the case of some pocket models, celluloid.

After 1951 the production of slide rules made from Astralon (sheet plastic material) was resumed. The stator and slide were milled to make the grooves and flanges. The first attempts were made to produce cursors by injection molding. After 1952 the stator and slide were made of Polystrol by injection molding. With the continuous improvement in techniques and equipment, the use of plastic was expanded and continued to the end of the slide rule era. The advanced state of its technology, its years of experience, and its knowledge of the requirements of the market, allowed the maturing of a balanced and successful product line at Faber-Castell. In addition to the wooden versions, slide rules with the old and dependable scale systems were now available in injection molded plastic with the designator "111/". For example the plastic version of the System Rietz became Model 111/87.

Many special purpose slide rules emerged, e.g., the Dywidag slide rule for concrete testing according to F. Kluge (2/62, later 57/62); Schirdewan's textile slide rule (57/74); Titscher's slide rule for welding (67/56); Max Schirmer's Demegraph for the graphic industry (2/66, later 111/66); the pocket slide rule for reinforced concrete (67/21); and so on. All these new developments came about during the period 1952-1956. Note that some special purpose slide rules aimed at limited markets were not made by injection molding, but rather milled from Astralon sheets. For example, in the cases of the Dywidag (2/62) and the Demegraph (2/66), there were sizes of the slide rule with their special scale divisions that made these slide rules different from the regular versions and, in such cases, the extra expense of developing an injection mold would not have been justified.

Model 3/11 (for reinforced concrete statics), replacing the System Torda, was developed in the late 1930s, and was made of wood. An expanded version (3/31) appeared in 1950. Both 3/11 and 3/31 were long (38 cm), had a stretched f_e scale, and C/D scales which extended to beyond the left and right indexes.

Because injection molded slide rules could be produced so economically, after 1952 it was possible to offer a series of inexpensive slide rules for students. In this series were: the Students' Rietz (57/87), the Students' Business (57/22), the Students' Advanced Rietz (57/88), the Students'

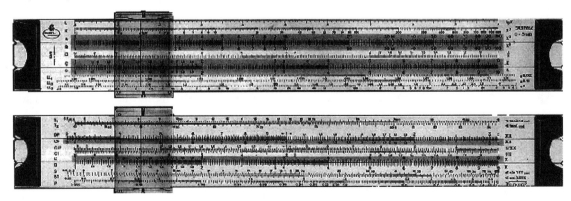

Fig.32. Faber-Castell's Schul-D-Stab (Model 52/82)

Log-Log (57/89), and later – after experience with more expensive two-sided slide rules – several duplex rules. These duplex rules included: the Mentor (52/80), the Novo-Mentor (52/81), and the Students' Duplo (52/82).

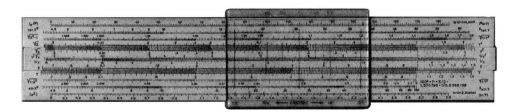

Fig.33. Faber-Castell's Mathema (Model 2/84)

For a student's slide rule, the Students' Duplo (52/82) had a very complete and sophisticated set of scales. The direct-reading trig and exponential scales, which eliminated the need to refer to tables, were welcomed by students. In addition, there were scales folded (displaced) on π. It should also be noted that Faber-Castell was the first slide rule maker to install the T2 scale (for tangent from 45° to 84.5°) on a student slide rule.

In 1952 the Castell-Mathema (2/84) with System Dr. Möller was developed. It appeared first in a special one-sided version and later (after 1968) as a duplex slide rule with metal "straps" (2/84N).

The following scales were found on the front of the Mathema: natural logs, tan-cot, the hyperbolic scale (Pythagorean scale II), the parabolic (square) scale, the reciprocal parabolic (square) scale, the reciprocal basic (single-cycle) scale, the circle scale (Pythagorean scale I), sin-cos, and natural logs. The following scales were found on the reverse side: the exponential scales for negative exponents, the hyperbolic tangent scale, the hyperbolic cosine scale, hyperbolic sine scale 1, hyperbolic sine scale 2, and the exponential scales for positive exponents. A vernier on the cursor extended the natural log scales to 10^8. All trigonometric scales used the 400^g (grade) system, which proved to be impractical since the 400^g system was not widely used and conversion from 360° to 400^g was time-consuming.

Paul Römer's "Master Calculator" (Rechenmeister, 2/77, 1956) pursued a new direction. It had interchangeable slides which permitted its use in various fields of expertise. Römer's slide rule failed to gain acceptance because of its unusual scale arrangement. The slide rule consisted of a stator, which measured 21x5 cm, a cursor, and several interchangeable slides that could be inserted in either side of the stator. On the edges of each slide were scales which matched corresponding scales on the stator and were arranged for specific special purposes. In the spaces between the scales there were setting-schemata which helped the user carry out calculations. There were slides for basic calculations, for the business applications, for calculation of area and cross-section, for trigonometry, for exponentiating, for electricity, and many others. The whole system worked on the setting of proportions.

The demand for duplex slide rules for special areas of expertise increased steadily. During the last decade of the slide rule era, Faber-Castell's top two slide rules were the Castell-Duplex (2/82, 1956) and the Castell-Novo-Duplex (2/83, 1962). As the result of structural improvements, Model 2/82 was succeeded by Model 2/82N, and Model 2/83 was followed by Model 2/83N. (See next page.) In the case of the Novo-Duplex, an old idea was adopted, i.e., extended Root Scales (W and W', folded at the square root of 10) were arranged along the two slide-stator interfaces on the back

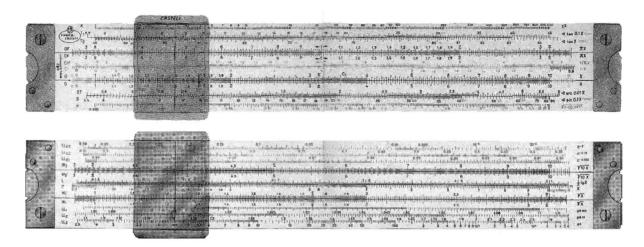

Fig.34. Faber-Castell's Novo-duplex (Model 2/83N) – top: front; bottom: back

side of the slide rule. There were also pocket versions of these slide rules (62/82 and 62/83, which later became 62/82N and 62/83N.)

After the mid-1950s there was an unprecedented increase in slide rule use. The slide rule had become a necessity for many professionals and a requirement in all schools and colleges. Modern business methods, lectures by experts, and "slide rule news letters" assured Faber-Castell a leading position among German slide rule makers that were engaged in both the domestic and foreign markets.

It eventually became obvious that the slide rule could be replaced by the electronic pocket calculator, but the actual change took place so rapidly that even Faber-Castell was taken by surprise. Faber-Castell, just like Aristo-Dennert & Pape, started making pocket calculators. In the case of Faber-Castell, production was carried out at same the factory (in Geroldsgrün) where slide rules were made. The result, a combination slide rule and pocket calculator, appeared in 1972. (They are now rare and prized by slide rule collectors.) The initial series of pocket calculators consisted of Models TR1, TR2, and TR3 – all with slide rules attached to the back. The cases and

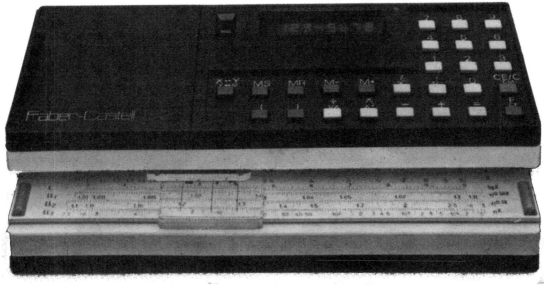

Fig.35. Faber-Castell's electronic calculator combined with slide rule

keys (with patented spring contacts) were made in-house. The chips and circuit boards were purchased from outside sources.

In the beginning the six exponential scales, the three trig scales, and the Pythagorean scale on the "built-in" slide rule were of use and desirable, since, for a while, Models TR1 and TR2 could only carry out the basic "four functions" (addition, subtraction, multiplication, and division). In the case of the TR3 these limitations did not apply, since a wider range of functions (excluding the P scale) was available.

Of the three slide rule/pocket calculator combinations, only the TR2 persisted. In the end the TR1N (which replaced the TR1), the TR3, and the TR4 (listed in order of their capabilities), plus the inexpensive Johann Faber 76, as well as the TRX (with power adapter) all emerged as pocket calculators without built-in slide rules.

Thus the very successful slide rule era finally ended for Faber-Castell. The manufacture of slide rules and even pocket calculators gradually ceased after 1975.

One very interesting footnote to history deserves to be mentioned: At the beginning of the 1970s, A.W. Faber-Castell signed a contract involving cooperation with a Soviet exporter-importer. In exchange for money, Faber-Castell delivered machines and tools and made know-how available. Faber-Castell's own specialists helped build a factory near Kharkov in the Ukraine. A year's production of the 25 cm plastic Darmstadt (i.e., 500,000 pieces) was set up. Later production of a duplex was set up. Whether these slide rules actually came into production cannot be confirmed from company records, but specimens have found their way into the hands of collectors. They are made of plastic and incorporate System Rietz and System Darmstadt.

Today the factory at Geroldsgrün, with its highly qualified personnel and modern machinery, is fully occupied with production of drawing boards, rulers, drafting templates, triangles, straight edges, writing instruments, and cosmetics. The factory is a component of the world famous firm A.W. Faber-Castell GmbH & Co. under the leadership of Count Anton Wolfgang von Faber-Castell.

IWA – Rechenschieberfabrik, Esslingen
IWA – F. Riehle Gmbh & Co, Denkendorf, Germany   IWA

This German slide rule maker occupies a special place among makers in that it was the leading source of special purpose slide rules, especially "sliding tables or nomographs." IWA was also successful in maintaining its position in the market for the so-called "data slides" and even today leads in this field in Europe.

IWA stands for **I**ngenieurerbüro für **w**irtschafliches **A**rbeiten (roughly the "Engineers' Office for Efficiency"). Slide rules marked IWA began to appear early in the 1920s; a company was founded later (in 1926) by Franz Riehle, and a factory was established.

The rapidly expanding product line included special purpose slide rules (made of plastic) and data slides for the revolution in industrial standards, especially in the field of mechanical engineering, which was itself expanding at that time. In most cases IWA collaborated with individual companies and inventors to develop a slide rule to solve a particular problem. Such rules were then custom made for the particular firm, and often the firm's name was printed on the device. Thus these slide rules became a form of advertising. In the beginning they were made of printed celluloid; later printed Astralon was used. In some cases the parts were glued together, but usually they were held together with hollow rivets. At first varnish was used to protect the scales or tables against wear; later, improved techniques involved cellophane coating. In contrast to the usual slide rule, the "data slide rule" (which by now was a uniformly adopted term) was defined by Harald Riehle as follows:

> "Each data slide rule serves only one special purpose. Not only logarithmic scales, but also scales with other functions are used – as necessary. Each scale is assigned a specific range. The scales are arranged under each other in a fixed order that is determined by the formula or mathematical function. In addition to the fixed scales, the data slide rule includes a slide with information elements that are essential to the operation of the slide rule. These elements are expressed predominantly in type style and serve to designate the purpose of the scale, to establish the units of measurement for the ranges, as well as the number of significant digits, and the decimal place for the individual ranges. Additional information elements can be supplied in the form of arrows, marks, graduations, pictograms, and diagrams. This list should make it clear how a data slide rule differs fundamentally from a conventional slide rule. In the case of a regular slide rule, the user must assign the decimal point, the units of measurement, and the context to one of the scales and apply his experience and knowledge to those tasks. " [82]

The Universal Pipe Flow Calculator (Model 06095) of Rötschow, shown below, is a typical example of one of IWA's data slide rules. This slide rule was equipped with two slides and two cursors. In addition to linear scales, it had various diagrams for calculations relating to its special applications.

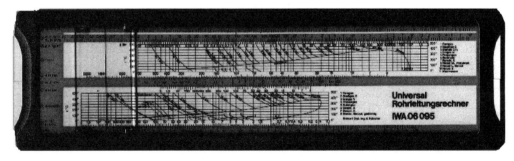

Fig.36. IWA pipeline slide rule (Model 06095)

In contrast with the famous makers of the well-known slide rules, IWA's special mission was, and still is, to make data slides (often in small runs) for specialists in various fields.

IWA's current product line even includes a simple pocket slide rule for engineers. It is based on the System Rietz, with scales folded at π. The IWA circular special purpose slide rules were also highly regarded, as was the IWAMATIC circular slide rule.

IWA-F.Riehle GmbH & Co, is still a family-owned firm and has concerned itself "with the transfer of information from the maker of industrial tools to the user and the access to the market in the post-slide rule era." The company's current prospectus lists well over 500 firms for whom IWA has made data slide rules, providing yet another special field of interest available to slide rule collectors.

The topic of "Data" slide rules (Tabellenschieber) and their foreign makers could become a whole chapter itself and a separate field for the slide rule collector. In every case such slide rules have had a chance to compete successfully against the pocket calculator because special slide rules and data slides offer the specialist an ideal way to deal immediately with special problems in his daily work.

Table slide rules and special slide rules for military purposes constitute another specialty that cannot be covered here – mainly because many of the necessary documents are not available.

IWA's predecessor in the field of special purpose slide rules was AWF, which is described on pages 47-48.

Löbker & Co. KG, Dresden-Klotzsche	**Löbker**
Meissner KG, Dresden-Klotzsche	**Meissner**
VEB Mantissa	**Mantissa**

This firm was founded by P. Löbker in 1932. At first it operated as a trading company, offering drawing instruments and a few slide rules. Löbker also operated a correspondence school. The firm's Rietz (Model 72/2) and "Löbkonorm" were well known but of lower quality. These slide rules were made of beechwood and had no spring in the stator floor. After the firm went bankrupt, in 1947, it was taken over by one of its workers, Horst Meissner, and renamed Meissner KG, Precision Intrument Factory. Meissner slide rules were sold mainly in Eastern Europe but were also known in Western Europe. They included two types of Rietz and two types of Darmstadt. These 25 cm, beechwood slide rules were of better quality. They had springs in the stator floor and cursors with framed glass. The Meissner line also included the "Darmstadt-Record" and school models. The Darmstadt-Record took the name of the Darmstadt system, but the slide rule was a double-sided model with the following scales: L, K, A/B, CI, C/D, LL1, LL2, LL3 (front) and P, S, ST, DF/CF, CIF (back). This slide rule clearly had many more scales than the traditional System Darmstadt.

In 1972 the firm was nationalized by the East German government and was renamed VEB Mantissa. However, the trademark "Meissner" was retained. The firm developed a few special purpose slide rules such as: Welding Cooling Time, Humidity, Navigation, the Variant, Organization, Pumps and Compressors, Galvanik, and Radiation Protection. All of these slide rules were made of plastic, as was the Model TRIM, a good quality and well-appointed slide rule. In addition there were special slide rules for Warsaw Pact artillery.

VEB Mantissa took over Meissner at a time when the slide rule was already in decline. However, the VEB continued to make slide rules and supply schools with the Mono-Rietz until 1984.

Albert Nestler AG, Lahr in Baden   **NESTLER**

In 1878 Nestler established a factory and thereafter claimed to be "the oldest specialty factory for slide rules of all kinds (Patent 173,660), fine drawing instruments, surveyors' poles, and stadia rods." Today, of course, we know that part of this claim was not valid, since Dennert & Pape had begun slide rule production in 1872, six years before Nestler.

The company's founders were Albert Nestler and Theophil Beck (Beck & Nestler). In 1881 Albert Nestler died and was succeeded by his sons Albert and Richard. From 1928 on, the company was known as Albert Nestler AG.

In the beginning, Nestler slide rules were made of beechwood and mahogany. The early scale configuration was based on the French Mannheim models, with A/B (two-cycle scales) and C/D (one-cycle scales) on the front of the slide rule. Scales S and T appeared on the back of the slide. Even before World War I, Nestler offered a wide range of slide rules. For example, the Nestler catalog of 1911-1912 lists 56 different models. Some were mahogany with celluloid scales. Even ivory and German Silver were used. A 40 cm Spanish Tacheometer (without cursor) made of German silver (Model 9a) cost 50 Marks, a very high price considering the salary levels that prevailed then.

The slide rules were listed beginning with Model 1, Model 1a, and so on, through Model 39. In addition to the general-purpose slide rules for engineers and merchants, there were special rules for reinforced concrete (System Prof. Nestle), lumber, chemists, textiles, and spinning. Nestler's "Präzision" had "extended" one-cycle scales which were divided in the middle (at the square root of 10) and arranged along both slide-stator interfaces on the front of the slide rule. The "Präzision" was offered in 15, 25, and 50 cm sizes and had effective scale lengths twice this long.

Nestler was the first firm to bring out a Rietz slide rule (in 1903); this was only one year after Max Rietz had been granted Patent 181110. The catalog of 1911-1912 shows a notable number of examples of System Rietz, more than any other maker at that time. The series included System Rietz in scale lengths of 15, 25, 35, 50, and 100cm, as well as four more versions with half-cylinder magnifying lenses on the cursor. The same catalog mentions the slide rule of Professor Eugen Hanauer (Model 34) "as one of the most versatile slide rules currently available." Made of mahogany, this slide rule's scales were celluloid and the cursor glasses were framed.

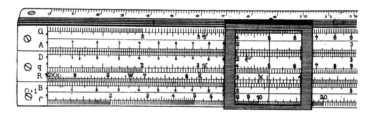

Fig.37. Nestler's "Hanauer" slide rule

The Hanauer had an unusual scale configuration. At the top of the front there was a two-cycle Q (for Quadrat) scale. Below it, along the upper slide-stator interface, there were two single-cycle scales (labeled A and D). There was a movable two-cycle "q" scale along the middle of the slide. An inverted single-cycle "R" scale and a single-cycle scale running from 1-10 (labeled B) were located along the lower slide-stator interface. Below that was a fixed three-cycle scale labeled C (cube scale). The lower edge of the stator carried a log-log scale from 1.1 to 60,000 arranged in two cycles. On the back of the slide there were trig scales S, ST, and T, plus a scale L for common logs. Noteworthy are the obviously unconventional scale designations that did not correspond to the usual scale designations that were in use at the time. Great importance was placed on the direct determination of squares and square roots, cubes and cube roots, and roots and powers of e that was possible with the Hanauer. The roots and powers of e were obtained with the use of a log-log scale, which was a remarkable feature for that time.

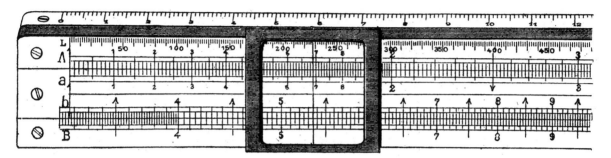

Fig.38. Nestler's "Tscherepaschinski" slide rule

In Models 26 and 26a we meet again the "System Tscherepaschinski," known both in Germany and France by the name of its Russian inventor.[93] These slide rules, too, were made of mahogany. The scales were celluloid, and the cursor glasses were framed. However, in this case there were two one-cycle scales along both the upper and the lower slide-stator interface, and the lower scale was folded at the square root of 10.

The 1938 catalog, which celebrated the firm's 60th anniversary, shows a line of slide rules that included: pocket slide rules made of celluloid; a machine time slide rule, a slide rule for calculating the weight of round, flat, and hexagonal bars of iron, aluminum, etc.; and a flyer's course calculator by Lieutenant E. Jason and Professor Dr. Schneider. Three versions of the new System Darmstadt (15, 25, and 50cm) were offered. These innovations showed that the period dominated by structural improvements in the slide rule had, by 1938, given way to a period dominated by changes in the scale systems. This was true for all German slide rule makers.

Especially interesting were two "double-sided" slide rules that were based on the American model but did not achieve their potential. Both were made of mahogany and had 25cm celluloid scales. Model 29 corresponded to System Rietz with added folded scales. Model 29a included extra exponential scales arranged on the front as follows: LL0, A/B, S, T, C/LL3, LL2, LL1. Until the beginning of World War II, Nestler exported slide rules to 60 countries and asserted that it was the "largest maker of slide rules in the world," a claim that was dubious. By 1945 Nestler's production facilities and valuable special equipment had either been damaged in the war or had been confiscated by the French occupation force. In 1950 Nestler made a new beginning. Tried-and-true models such as System Rietz, System Darmstadt, and the Elektro remained in the product line. They were available in wood and in plastic. After 1962 the product line was widened to include such double-sided slide rules as the Polymath-Duplex, the Multimath-Duplex, the Rietz Duplex, the "school series" (Alpha, Beta, Gamma, and Delta), as well as special purpose slide rules for reinforced concrete, surveying, electronics, and chemistry.

Nestler's "top of the line" slide rule was the Multimath-Duplex (Model 0292), which had a total of 28 scales corresponding to the demands of the technical user. A special feature was a one-cycle

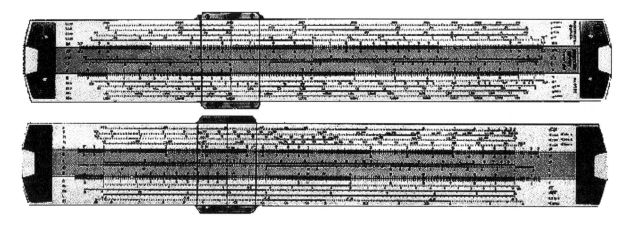

Fig.39. Nestler's Multimath slide rule

scale that was divided at the square root of 10 and arranged in two lines along the back of the lower stator rail.

Toward the end of the slide rule era Nestler was offering 30 standard size slide rules plus seven demonstration models; it participated in the "boom times" of the 1960s. For Nestler, too, the early 1970s stood out as the end of the slide rule era. Production was curtailed and finally discontinued. Nestler remained for a long time a well-known and capable producer and distributor of drafting machines and instruments, but in 1994 the company went out of business. Both the shift from the slide rule to the pocket calculator and the shift from drafting machines to computer-aided design (CAD) probably contributed to the demise of the company.

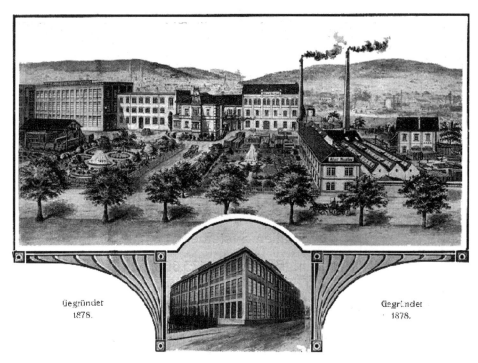

Gegründet 1878.

Gegründet 1878.

Gesamtansicht meines Fabrikanwesens nach Photographie

8668 qm Fläche.

Fig.40. View of Nestler factory

R. Reiss GmbH Fabrik technischer Artikel Liebenwerda   REISS
Reiss, Bad Liebenwerda, Germany   REISS
Reiss, Bad Liebenwerda, DDR   REISS
Reiss Zeichentechnik GmbH, Bad Liebenwerda   REISS

The firm was founded in 1882, by Robert Reiss, as a mail-order house for office and drawing supplies. Over time Reiss developed into a well-known "maker of precision instruments (such as theodolites, stadia, and planimeters), traditional drafting equipment (adjustable drafting tables, track system drafting machines, blue print machines), and, last not but not least, slide rules of various kinds and models – including some for military purposes."

Fig.41.
Robert Reiss
(1843-1911)

In 1899, the framework was established for making slide rules at Reiss when two cabinetmakers took up the production of surveyors' rods and leveling rods. Gradually a varnishing shop, a repair shop, and a machine shop were added. In the course of the next three decades, Reiss grew to become the largest industry in the region. It employed several hundred workers, had a wide product line, and exported to all over the world. (However, the slide rules probably accounted for only 6 or 7% of Reiss' entire sales.) The creativity of Robert Reiss, his son and successor Paul, and their co-workers was noteworthy. This creativity was reflected in the many patents (especially for drafting machines) that the firm was awarded.

At first Reiss sold slide rules made by other companies. Reiss's mail order offerings as early as 1902 included the following slide rules made by Dennert & Pape: Model 2815 (a 25cm slide rule with Dr. Frank's system and an effective scale length of 50 cm), Model 1041 (25cm, A/B, R, C/D plus S and T), Model 1042 (the 50cm version of 1041), Model 2812 (the 12.5cm "Simplex"), and Model 2813 (the 25cm "Simplex"). The same catalog included the following slide rules made by Faber: Model 1045 (25cm, beech wood, celluloid scales) and Model 1147 (for foresters). The earliest slide rules made by Reiss appeared in 1912. As was customary at that time, these slide rules were made of boxwood. Later mahogany and then walnut were used. Reiss was one of the companies to make slide rules from light metal and German silver. More and more Reiss made its own slide rules and widened the product line. In the early 1920s, Reiss tried hard to achieve parity with the "Big Three" German slide rule makers, i.e., Faber-Castell, D&P, and Nestler. Reiss, independently or in collaboration with specialists, developed new slide rules which introduced certain new concepts. Most of the innovations were based on the idea of the "extended scale."

Some of these models from the 1920s should be mentioned: Model 1141 (the Stellfix T, 25cm, mahogany, with standard, square, and cubic scales with effective lengths of 50cm) and Model 1141a (the 12.5cm version of 1141) were both for engineers. Model 1143 (Stellfix K, 25cm) was for merchants. The introduction of these slide rules attracted much attention, and they were discussed in the *Zeitschrift für Mechanik und Präzision* in 1923-24. These slide rules came with a specially designed frameless cursor (the Phoenix) which permitted the hairline to be adjusted to true vertical and allowed the lens to be replaced. (DRP 364364, 1922) The Stellfix series was still included in a price list from 1952. The REISS line of slide rules also included Seifert's Surveying Slide Rule (Model 1145, the "Py-Lo") which had extended scales and eight surveyor's and architect's scales along the slanted edge, a feature much noticed by specialists who would use the rule. There was also Rathe's machine-time slide rule. Finally, there was the Phönix series which, among other features, had a notch or "finger grip" at both ends of lower edge of the stator. According to the catalog, this notch "made it possible to grip the slide rule very securely and, thereby, contributed to smooth slide operation and exact slide settings."

One very different slide rule was the System Cuntz. This was a pocket model with a very wide upper section which carried 11 scales. The cursor hairline was used to relate these scales to the one-cycle C/D scales. Below the C/D scales there was an inverted D scale (DI). The 11 scales on the upper section included two extended square scales, three extended cube scales, plus scales for the circumference of a circle, area of a circle, and the trig functions. The effective length of the C and D scales was 25cm. The scale designations at the left and right scale ends were well conceived but unconventional for the time. This and other new creations (the Stellfix and the Phönix) did not help REISS gain on its German competition, and the company got into financial difficulties at a time of worldwide depression. As a result, in 1928 the company was changed from a family-owned operation into a limited liability company under the control of Gebr. Wichmann of Berlin, a famous mail-order house for drafting instruments. During the time of the Third Reich, Reiss concentrated more and more on armament – in particular telescopic gun sights, telescopes/periscopes, and stereotelescopes. However, the production of slide rules, including military models, continued.

Reiss survived World War II undamaged. However, because it was in Russian-occupied Germany, Reiss was completely dismantled in 1945, and in 1947 it became a state-run business. It exported considerable numbers of slide rules to the Eastern European countries, but Reiss was also well known in Western Europe. These post-war Reiss models included the following light metal slide rules: Model 3203 (Rietz), Model 3204 (Darmstadt), Model 3205 (Elektro), and Model 3223 (the "Progress," a further refinement of two of Reiss's own ideas). Reiss slide rules of Astralon (known as Decelith in East Germany) included Model 3214 (Disponent), Model 3214 (Darmstadt-Record), Model 3236 (Darmstadt), Model 3212 (Darmstadt-Rietz), and Model 3227 (Reiss-duplex). This latter slide rule had 32 scales, probably the largest number of scales on any known slide rule. The following scales were on the front: LL00, LL01, LL02, LL03, DF/CF, CIF, BI, CI, C/ D, LL3, LL2, LL1, LL0. The following scales were on the back: K, T1, T2, DI, A/Sh1, Sh2, Th,S', C/, D, S, P, ST, L. These were virtually all the scales in common use that could be physically accommodated on a slide rule, but the clarity of the rule suffered from the crowding.

In 1972, as part of an affiliation with the state-owned firm Robotron and because of a new emphasis on the manufacture of plotters, Reiss turned over slide rule production to a new firm, VEB-Mantissa, which at that time also took over the products of Meissner. Mantissa remained in production until 1984.

Today Reiss continues under Gebr. Wichmann as a very capable and modern producer and distributor of office and computer furniture as well as drafting machines and tables.

France

GRAPHOPLEX Paris, France

GRAPHOPLEX

The great tradition of the 19th century French slide rule makers was continued by Graphoplex, although the company did not begin the manufacture of slide rules until 1941. Its slide rules were, as might be expected at that time, made from plastic stock or sheets, and its assortment of slide rules suited the European market.

The single-sided Graphoplex slide rules included: the Rietz, which came in 12.5 cm (Model 612), 15 cm (615), 25 cm (620) and 50 cm (6250) versions; the Electric-Log-Log in 12.5 cm (643), 25 cm (640), and 50 cm (6245) versions; the STATOS Béton Armé in 25 cm (660); the 25 cm Commercial (645), the 25 cm Géomètre (630); the 25 cm Rolinea; "an old friend," the System Beghin [80], in the form of a students' slide rule with a pair of scales folded at the square root of 10; and the 25 cm System Darmstadt (647).

Graphoplex also had some very well-designed, double-sided slide rules including: the Neperlog (690); the Neperlog-Hyperbolic (691); the Radian-Log (695); the Decilog (699); the Electronicien (698) for radio and telecommunications; the Tecnilog (694), and the school model Trigo-Fix (696).

The quality of the Graphoplex slide rules was good. Only the expert user noticed that the scale marks were not, as was usual, incised, but were applied by a photochemical process. Because of this, the scale markings on the upper surface of the slide rule were not deep and thus protected against rough handling, and these scales did not hold up as well as incised files. Also worth noting was the use of special scale designations. For example, the main scales A/B and C/D were unconventionally designated B^2/b^2 and b/B. The trigonometric scales on the System Rietz, the Electro-Log-Log, and the Rolinea were available with trigonometric scales in degrees and minutes or in decimal form.

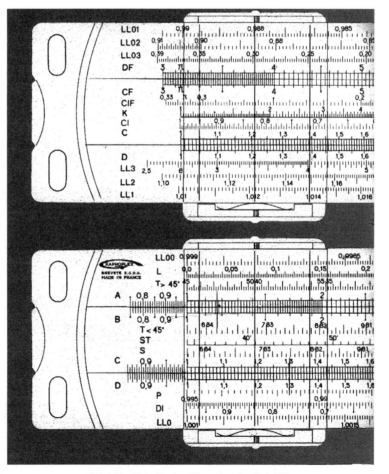

Fig.42. Graphoplex Neperlog (Model 690)

The trade mark Graphoplex later appeared on a well-known line of rulers, templates, straight edges, triangles, curves, etc.

United States

Eugene Dietzgen Co, Chicago, U.S.   **DIETZGEN**

This firm, a well-known producer and supplier of slide rules in the U.S., was founded in 1885 by the German immigrant Eugene Dietzgen, who started offering slide rules around 1887. In 1893 he acquired a factory through a merger with the Peter Heer Co., a maker of drawing instruments, and in 1906 a new production site was built in Chicago. In a catalog dated 1907/1908, the Eugene Dietzgen Co. represented itself as the producer and importer of drawing materials and surveying instruments with sales offices in Chicago, New York, San Francisco, and New Orleans.

A study made by Bruce Babcock [72] reports a total of 154 different model numbers and variations offered by Dietzgen over the decades, with the firm making some slide rules and importing others. Dietzgen expanded its line with German slide rules, especially (after 1910) rules made by A. W. Faber (later Faber-Castell). This cooperation continued, with interruptions, until the end of the slide rule era. In 1909 Dietzgen acquired the drafting instrument factory of Eichmüller & Co. in Nürnberg. In the 1930s this factory began to make metal slide rules, mainly for Dietzgen.

It would be difficult even to begin to describe all the Dietzgen slide rules; however a few of the more important ones will be mentioned.

By 1902, Mannheim slide rules of the "Union Series" were available. These included #1776 (12.5 cm) and #1777 (25 cm). In addition there were the "Mack Improved Slide Rules," which incorporated the spiral springs that connected the two stator halves (a feature patented in 1898). This series included models 1764 (12.5 cm), 1764L (20 cm), 1765 (25 cm), 1765L (40 cm), and 1767 (50 cm), all of which were Mannheim slide rules. After 1904 Dietzgen offered a Multiplex series that consisted of five models (12.5 – 50 cm). The scales on the Multiplex slide rule differed in only minor ways from the scales on the previous Dietzgen slide rules. Dietzgen also offered some rules that were actually made by A.W. Faber. These included models 1780 - 1784 (25 cm) and 1785 (50 cm). Finally, there was model 1787, the Scofield-Thacher or "Engineers' slide rule." This was a "pseudo-double-sided" slide rule, with a separate slide plus four scales on each side, and no cursor.

For its time, the above was a noteworthy line of slide rules; it was sustained, however, only until around 1920. The period between 1920 and 1940 was a time of stagnation for the company. There were significant gaps in its product line, and the (Mannheim) scale system was becoming "old fashioned." Through patents, its powerful domestic competitor Keuffel & Esser blocked Dietzgen's production of the double-sided slide rules that were so important in the American market. It was not until 1943-44 that Dietzgen, in spite of the claims of K&E, obtained patents (2369819 and 2407338) that permitted the firm to make the modern double-sided slide rule. These were offered as the Maniphase series. By now the log-log scales were a component of the scale systems that were in demand. Even a log-log vector slide rule was offered. After World War II Dietzgen once again obtained some of its slide rules from Faber-Castell. In 1970 these included models 1734 (Decimal trig log log), 1741 (in the Novo-duplex style), 1765 (BasiK) and 1739 (Clear-scale) – the latter two being inexpensive student rules offered in the U.S.

Eugene Dietzgen Co. was eventually sold to a private investment group and renamed Dietzgen Corporation. It remains in business but with new product lines.

KEUFFEL & ESSER , Hoboken, N.J., United States   K&E

Without doubt this firm was one of the most significant producers of a broad range of high quality slide rules. The historical record shows that slide rules were not made and were little used in America until the end of the 1800s when Keuffel & Esser began selling, and later making, slide rules.

The firm was founded in 1867 by William J. D. Keuffel and Herman Esser as a mail-order house for art and drafting supplies, which the company produced as well as imported. The company's first catalog appeared in 1868. It was followed by 45 editions through 1976. At first (1887) K&E offered a Gunter (model 1745) and a Mannheim (model 1746). The makers of these slide rules are not known. Beginning around 1891, finished slide rules were imported from Dennert & Pape in Germany. Around 1895 K&E began to import blanks from Dennert & Pape and finish them in the U.S. By 1900 it started to produce its own celluloid-faced, mahogany slide rules. [84] About that time K&E built a factory in Hoboken, New Jersey, that remained the location of the company's headquarters until the end. (Production of plastic slide rules began in the 1950s at the Salisbury Products Division, Lakeville, Connecticut, a K&E-owned subsidiary.) [85]

When K&E started making slide rules, it adopted the manufacturing methods used for the imported German slide rules. Even German scale dividing machines were imported from D&P and

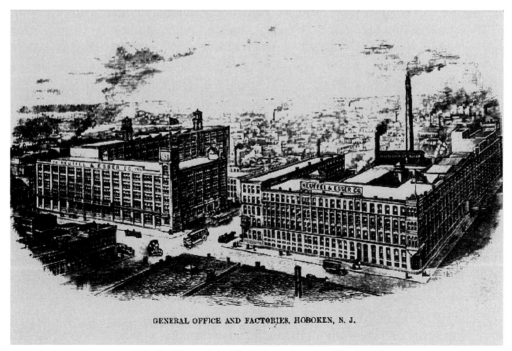

GENERAL OFFICE AND FACTORIES, HOBOKEN, N. J.

Fig.43. View of Keuffel & Esser factory around 1900

installed. As advisor to K&E, the already-mentioned William Cox, a descendant of a family of English instrument makers, had substantial influence on the K&E product line.

In addition to making the slide rule well known in the U.S., Cox helped in the acceptance of the Mannheim rule and also acquired patents for individual scale variants. His most important "invention" was a two-sided slide rule with a two-sided cursor. For this innovation K&E was granted a very important patent (#460930) in 1891. This patent guaranteed K&E a great advantage in the development of this type of slide rule and determined the subsequent direction of most American slide rule production. Keep in mind that the Japanese did not bring out their own double-sided models until 1929, and the German double-sided slide rules came along even later (1948), during the post-World War II recovery. In the 1930s, Nestler and Dennert & Pape product lines included only a few double-sided models similar to the K&E duplex.

From the time that K&E first made its own slide rules (around 1900), the firm manufactured and actively marketed both basic forms of the slide rule, i.e., the one-sided "Polyphase Mannheim type" and the two-sided "Polyphase Duplex type." These slide rules were protected by various additional patents also relating to scale configuration. Such protection was possible in North America, but not in Germany. It is worth noting that these scale configurations were so advanced that they were used until the end of the slide rule era. Although System Rietz (ca. 1904) and System Darmstadt (ca. 1935) were marketed by the German makers and were well known in Europe, these scale systems did not appear on any K&E slide rules because any scale configurations that went beyond the basic "Mannheim" were always marketed on Duplex rules.

K&E slide rules were marketed mainly in the U.S. Few were exported. This was partly due to the huge size of the domestic market and also to the fact that the Duplex slide rule became popular in Europe only after World War II. An existing tabulation of K&E slide rules lists a total of 223 different K&E slide rule models during the period 1887-1955. [86]

Before describing K&E slide rules further, it might be helpful to comment on the K&E model numbering system, or rather the three numbering systems that were used. Before 1900, slide rules had numbers in the "1700" series, i.e., all slide rule model numbers began with "17.." followed by two digits. These model numbers rarely (if ever) appeared on the slide rule. From 1900 to the late 1950s, model numbers were in the "4000" and "4100" series. The "4000" series tended to be general purpose slide rules and the "4100" series tended to be special purpose slide rules and, later, plastic slide rules. Gradually the suffixes 1, 2, 3, 4, and 5 were adopted to indicate size (5, 8, 10, 16, and 20 inches respectively). Thus 4081-5 indicated the 20 inch version of model 4081 (a log-log decitrig duplex). The prefix N was often added (or removed) to indicate that small changes had been made in a model. (For some reason, during this period, three plastic "Doric's" were assigned numbers in the 900 series.) Finally, a third system was adopted sometime between 1955 and 1964 when bound catalogs were no longer issued. These numbers were in the "68 1000" series. [87] This system is less well understood because the catalogs were unbound ("loose-leaf"), they were updated one page at time, and replaced pages were rarely preserved.

A catalog from 1949 serves well for considering the most important K&E slide rules. The catalog's "Polyphase slide rule Mannheim-Type" was the original standard model. It is offered in 25 cm (Model 4054-3) and 50 cm (Model 4054-5) sizes. The scale configuration was A/B, CI, CI/D, K – with scales S, L, and T appearing on the back of the slide. In addition there were inch and centimeter scales on the slanted upper and lower edges respectively.

The same scale arrangement, without the inch and centimeter scales, appeared on Model 4054. The "Favorite" (Model 4056) has scales A/B,C/D plus S, L, T. Of course one can argue that K&E

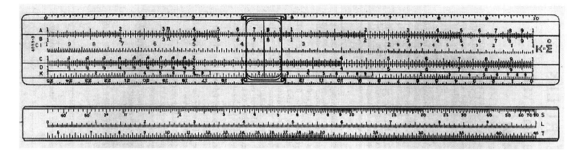

Fig.44. Keuffel & Esser Mannheim (Model 4053-3)

used the term "Mannheim" in a rather broad sense because (to be absolutely correct) these scale configurations did not match those on the original Mannheim. Model 4058N ("The Beginners") was offered "for the use of beginners to enable them to become familiar with the slide rule."

All the slide rules in the Polyphase group had the same patented mechanism that permitted the user to adjust the slide action by means of screws in the back of the stator.

Polyphase Duplex Trig (Model 4070-3) and Polyphase Duplex Decitrig (Model 4071-3) were both 25 cm (10 inch) slide rules. The two differed only in the markings on the trig scales. Model 4070-3 was marked in degrees and minutes; Model 4071-3 was marked in degrees and decimals thereof (hence the term DeciTrig). One thing that is striking is the presence of scales (DF, DF, and CIF) that are folded on π. This was something that became accepted only much later in Europe because of the delayed adoption of the double-sided slide rule there.

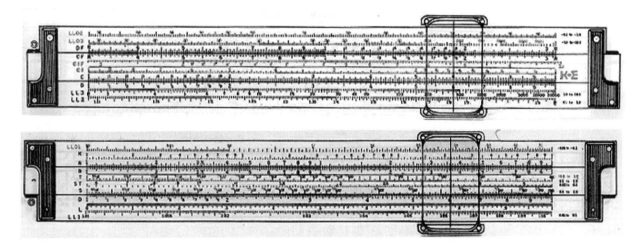

Fig.45. Keuffel & Esser log-log duplex (Model 4081-3)

There were six other models in the standard duplex series, and they all carried the six log-log scales LL1, LL2, LL3, LL01, LL02, and LL03. These slide rules were the:

LogLog Duplex Trig in 10 inches (Model 4080-3) and 20 inches (Model 4080-5)

LogLog Duplex Decitrig in 10 inches (N4081-3) and 20 inches (N4081-5)

LogLog Duplex Vector in 10 inches (N4083-3) and 20 inches (N4083-5). The latter two models had two-part hyperbolic sine scales (Sh1 and Sh2) as well as a hyperbolic tangent scale (Th).

All the above duplex models had a patented mechanism (i.e., screws imbedded in the stator bars) for adjusting the slide tension and the stator alignment.

The 1949 catalog included a limited range of pocket slide rules, including two single-sided models (4150-1 and 4161-1) and two duplex models (4168 and 4181-1). The scale configuration of the latter corresponded to the Loglog Decitrig Duplex (4081-3). In addition, there were three five-inch single-sided rules from the high quality "Everthere" series (4097B, 4097C, and 4097D).

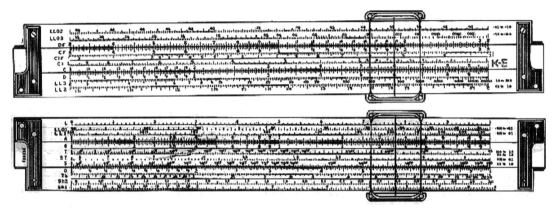

Fig.46. Keuffel & Esser log-log duplex vector (Model N 4083-3)

What was remarkable was the limited number of special purpose slide rules that were offered. There were two stadia rules (10 and 20 inch), a surveyor's rule, a "sewer" rule, the "Roylance Electrician's Rule," a chemist's duplex, and the "Cooke Radio Slide Rule."

An American specialty was a leather slide rule case with flap-and-strap closure. Such a case could be hung from the user's belt by a loop with a swivel hook. American college students who hung their slide rules from their belts (like Colt revolvers) were typical and unmistakable.

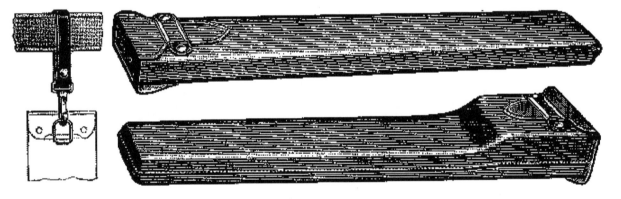

Fig.47. Two K&E leather slipcases and a belt loop

It must be acknowledged that K&E was one of the largest producers of slide rules in the world. The company is said to have made over 10 million slide rules. [88] Of course the number of slide rules made by Hemmi and the German makers is not known, but estimates are much lower than 10 million.

There is a very interesting study of K&E by Wayne Feely [89] that also highlights the concerns facing all slide rule makers at the time. Beginning in 1956, the company had shifted from mahogany rules to plastic rules. (In 1956 83.3% were mahogany, and 16.7% were plastic. In 1967 44.4%

were mahogany, and 55.6% plastic.) The competition had become very strong. Pickett had 23% of the market, Post had 20%, and Dietzgen had 7%. [90] In 1970 K&E made a forceful move to again dominate the U.S. slide rule market, even though the threat from pocket calculators was already evident. K&E formed a "slide rule committee" which was charged to make recommendations for the improvement of the slide rule and for more effective marketing of the slide rule.

The committee's recommendations for the improvement of the slide rule required nothing strikingly new. For example, there was a recommendation to change the decades-old length standards, i.e., from 5 inches to 8, from 10 to 12, and from 20 to 16. The report also recommended "easy to read" scales and scales folded on the square root of 10 instead of π – which were certainly not new or decisive ideas. The outcome of all this was the design for a new model called the KE-LON. In the end the KE-LON actually ignored some of the committee's recommendations. The prototype was well made, but the slide rule was overburdened with 30 scales and, for that reason, was difficult to read. The KE-LON never went into production, and the very sound plan to make all slide rules by injection molding techniques was never implemented. It was too late! K&E stopped making slide rules early in the 1970s. [91]

Pickett & Eckel, Santa Barbara, U.S.

P & E

PICKETT

Pickett & Eckel was founded in 1943. The name of the firm was changed from Pickett & Eckel to Pickett, after Eckel left the firm around 1949. (After Eckel left P&E, he produced some round slide rules under his own name, but they were not very successful.) Pickett started in Chicago, but moved manufacturing to Alhambra, California in 1950. In 1964 the company moved to Santa Barbara. [95]

This American slide rule maker and its slide rules will be described in rather general terms because the firm issued very few catalogs and such catalogs are now virtually non-existent.

The first P&E slide rule was made of cardboard and appeared in 1943, during the war. This rule was almost identical to its double-sided, metal successor (the DeciPoint), which appeared in 1946. The DeciPoint was followed by a long series of double-sided, metal slide rules. Later there were plastic and one-sided models.

In the beginning, the duplex slide rules were made of a magnesium alloy. The exposed edges were dull gray, and they tended to become oxidized and powdery. The magnesium alloy was then replaced with aluminum, which worked splendidly. A special feature of some of the aluminum slide rules was a pair of tiny springs which were tucked in one stator rail under the stator bars. These springs regulated the slide action.

Around 1950, P&E introduced slide rules with black markings on a yellow background. This was promoted as a high-contrast combination that was easier to read. Model numbers for such slide rules carried the suffix ES (for "Eye-Saver" yellow). The traditional black-on-white was also available. These carried the suffix "T" (for "Traditional" white). Also the cursors were modified several times and adapted to the prevailing technology (as was the case with most other makers.) [94]

As mentioned above, the first P&E duplex was called the DeciPoint, and it offered the following bewildering scale configuration: (from top downward) a three-part cubic scale, L/, T1, T2, ST, S, CI, C/D, and a two-part square root scale.

The Model 500 (later 803) and the Model 902 (later 1010) were also well known and widely distributed. There were also several special purpose Pickett slide rules – especially for the armed forces. Today these are highly valued by collectors and command high prices.

Without doubt, Pickett & Eckel was the most important maker of light metal slide rules. The models and versions numbered in the hundreds. There were at least 35 model numbers and eight different variations that reflected changes in construction over time. [94]

Pickett was very aggressive about introducing its slide rule into high schools so that students who went on to college would tend to buy advanced Pickett instead of K&E slide rules. Because of this aggressive promotion of slide rule instruction in high schools, today there are far more Pickett demonstration rules and projection rules in the hands of collectors than there are K&E demonstration rules.

The Pickett family sold the business in 1964. After 1974, the Pickett Company moved to Mexico, where the firm made drafting supplies.

Sterling Plastics, Mountainside, NJ, U.S.   STERLING
Division of Borden Chemical, Borden Inc.

This company was founded in 1938 for the manufacture of drafting instruments. In 1961 plastic slide rules were first added to the product line. Sterling established a reputation for very economical models that were sold in blister packs. Sterling became best known for its basic Mannheim slide rules and for so-called "metric conversion rules" which were used to convert U.S. units of measurement into metric units. The extent of the entire Sterling product line can no longer be determined, but it included a wide range of economical models. There was also a series of excellent slide rules, especially duplex models, which carried the trade name "ACUMATH."

Czechoslovakia

Logarex, Ceske Budejovice, Czechoslovakia   LOGAREX

This firm was originally owned by an F. Tajman, who started the company before World War II as a small factory and retail shop specializing in drawing instruments. After the war, the company changed hands several times. Until 1948 Logarex belonged to a partly state-owned company called Lyra (no connection with a pencil factory of the same name) that made wooden picture frames. From 1948 to 1950 Logarex belonged to L&C Hardtmuth (which made Koh-I-Noor Pencils), with headquarters in Vienna and Budweis. A Rietz and an Elektro model were made with the Hardmuth trademark. It was around 1949 that the company began to make slide rules; later production was continued under the trademark Logarex after the company was nationalized.

The last company catalog showed 19 models, all made of plastic, with model numbers in the "2700 series." These included the following single-sided slide rules: the Darmstadt Logaron (12.5cm), the Darmstadt (25cm), the Rietz (10, 12.5, and 50cm), a machining time slide rule, a steam water slide rule, a gas slide rule, a "Precision" (25cm), and a decibel Neper (15cm). The double-sided slide rules included: a Rietz, a Darmstadt, an Exponent (12.5cm, 25cm), System Trig (25cm), Studio-Engineering (25cm), and Premiant (25cm).

Logarex slide rules were sold mainly in Eastern Europe; few were exported to Western Europe. Logarex continued on as a maker of rulers, straight edges, and templates.

Denmark

DIWA – Regnestockefabrik, Gentofte, Denmark　　　　　DIWA

This factory was established in 1924 as a small shop for making measuring devices and slide rules. In the course of time. DIWA established itself as a well-regarded maker of slide rules, especially in Scandinavian countries, although DIWA slide rules were exported to other countries, too.

The slide rules that were offered after World War II (especially those offered toward the end of the slide rule era) comprised a tight series of 16 models. Among them were the following single-sided models: Rietz-Ideal 1-1 (with Rietz scales all on the front surface), Rietz 501-1 (with the classical Mannheim configuration with trig scales on the back of the slide), Darmstadt 551-1, Elektro 511-1, and Businessman 541. The double-sided DIWA slide rules included the Teknilog 710 and Polylog 720. There were also corresponding pocket models: 601-1, 611-1, and 641-1. Students at the university and teachers' colleges in Denmark were required to use the Rietz-Ideal slide rule, and, according to information from DIWA, there were 100,000 DIWA slide rules in use in high schools.

The Teknilog and the Polylog differed only in the trig scale locations. In the case of the Teknilog, the S, ST, and T scales were on the front of the stator; in the case of the Polylog, these scales were on the back of the slide. In the beginning of the 1970's DIWA added three double-sided slide rules: the Ideal 701 (with D/F and C/D on the back); the Combilog 730 (with the corresponding pocket model 815), the Businessman 741 (which replaced the one-sided 541); and the pocket model 641. There were two special slide rule manuals in Danish: one by Arne Ostergaard for the Rietz-Ideal and one by Einar Anderson for the Polylog.

The DIWA-Regnestok-Fabrik no longer exists as an independent operation.

There was an additional Danish slide rule maker who used the brand name UTO. This firm's slide rules were of good quality and are sought by collectors. It is known that UTO made Rietz, Electro, and Darmstadt/Duplolog slide rules. Unfortunately nothing more is known about this company.

Hungary

GAMMA Müszaki RT. Budapest, Hungary   GAMMA

István Juhasz was born in 1894 in Kassa, Hungary (now Kaschau, Slovakia). Trained as a mechanical engineer, in 1920 he and his brother Zoltan began what was to later become an important factory for precision mechanical and optical instruments. For example, in the 1930s Gamma (in cooperation with Bofors) was well known for a highly developed, precision, optical firing data calculator for anti-aircraft guns. This device was exported to many countries.

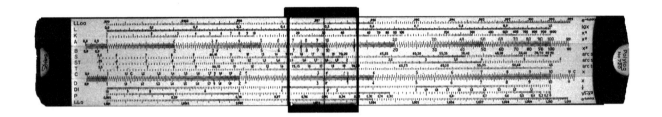

Fig.48. The DIWA Polylog (front)

In the early 1930s Gamma also started making slide rules. There were pocket, standard, and 50cm models with both System Rietz and System Darmstadt, all of good quality. After World War II the main Gamma slide rule was the Gamma Normal (Model 2512), which had typical Darmstadt markings, was made of pearwood or beech, was 25cm long, and had a frameless cursor. Also available was the "Kis Gamma" ("Little Gamma," Model 1252), which was 12.5cm, made of wood, and had a frameless cursor and a Gamma slide rule for machining time called the "Robot."

In 1939-1940, Gamma facilitated a delivery of Faber-Castell slide rules to the Hungarian army. This delivery involved a 50cm pearwood artillery slide rule (Bemérö logarléc). The construction was typical of Faber-Castell. The slide rule was based on a circle divided into 6400 mils. The device was used for the conversion of rectangular map coordinates into polar coordinates for the gun and vice versa, as well as for evaluating the sinus function for right and oblique triangles.

The Gamma factory was put under communist government control in 1947, and, as a "person out of favor," István Juhasz was no longer allowed to set foot in his famous tool works. He died impoverished in 1981.

After 1953 the Gamma slide rule program was continued by a new, state-controlled, firm called Iskoli Taneszközök Gyára. In the end only the System Rietz slide rule remained in production. Most were made of mahogany and the celluloid scales, in black and white only, were of poor quality. The Gamma logo was not used much longer.

Italy

Vittorio Martini, Bologna, Italy

V. Martini Antica Fabricca

This firm was founded in 1866, with headquarters in Bologna, as a factory for "articulo tecnici di precisione per disegno." It began with the production of drawing instruments that were in demand at that time. The wide-ranging product line included straight edges, rulers, and triangles. While it is not known when the company started making slide rules, there is a notice in the last Martini catalog that the 9th Congress for Italian Engineers and Architects in October 1889 had expressed high praise for the production of the "Martini Slide Rule." Therefore, it appears that this company, like most European slide rule makers, began making slide rules in the late 1800s.

The first Martini slide rule was made of beechwood and corresponded to the Mannheim system. Even at this time the slide rule carried the trade mark "Antica Fabricca Vittorio Martini," a mark that was on Martini slide rules until the end. The catalog from 1970 shows 13 slide rules. There were five Rietz models in the 12.5 length, one 15cm and one 25cm, a line Elettro (2) in 12.5cm, a Elettro Cosfi (2) in 12.5cm and 25cm, a Darmstadt (1) in 12.5cm, and, last but not least, a Universal in 12.5cm. (All models were made of American vinylite.)

The last mentioned Universal had an unusual scale arrangement. There were only two fixed scales on the lower stator, a one-cycle and a logarithmic scale. On a very wide slide were K, S&T&arc, T, S, and a one-cycle C, certainly making this slide rule unusual and difficult to use.

It is remarkable how many pocket models appear in the 1970 list. Note also that Martini did not follow the contemporary trend towards double-sided slide rules. Instead the company confined itself to the conservative Rietz and Darmstadt systems.

Martini is now a well-known maker of straight edges, rulers, T-squares, triangles, templates, and drafting tables.

Japan

The Hemmi Seisakusho Co. Ltd., Tokyo

SUN HEMMI

The Hemmi Seisakusho Co. Ltd., Shibuya, Tokyo, Japan, was founded in 1895. Around that time two Japanese scientists returned from a trip overseas and brought with them two North American Mannheim-type slide rules. This stimulated a group of Japanese craftsmen to begin making slide rules. After a few years, Jiro Hemmi (1878-1953) took charge of this group and, until the middle of the twentieth century, led the company that bears his name to become one of the top slide rule makers.

Fig.49.
Jiro Hemmi
(1878-1953)

In the first years, the Hemmi slide rules were made of boxwood with engraved, black scales. Later the celluloid scales developed in Germany (by Dennert & Pape) were applied to the Hemmi slide rules. In 1912, after many experiments, it was decided to apply celluloid veneer to bamboo. This construction was used until the end of the slide rule era, even after

Fig.50. View of Hemmi factory in Seitama circa 1940

Hemmi had introduced some plastic slide rules (after 1961). Bamboo was very resistant to climatic changes, was relatively light, and offered a superior slide action, and the Hemmi catalog of 1941 still shows only bamboo slide rules. In the beginning single-sided Mannheim slide rules were offered in various sizes and with various features. After 1912 Hemmi was granted several patents for double-sided slide rules and well as for the processing of bamboo wood. In 1917 the trademark "SUN" (with sunrise pictures on both sides of the name) was registered, and a new scale-engraving procedure was patented in 1923. In 1940 the company moved into a new factory building in Seitema (near Tokyo). The catalog at this time offered 67 models, beginning with Model 1, which was part of the so-called "Normal" series. This series included more than 20 different models with various features. In general these were Mannheim variants with the standard A/B and C/D scales, as well as scales S, T, and L. With few exceptions, all the single-sided slide rules had the same characteristic cursor with a lens frame that was open to the left. It is also surprising that, as late as 1940, some models were still offered with cursors containing a decimal indicator, something that had long been abandoned in Europe. It should be noted that by 1943, 11 to 15 year old students were required to learn to use the slide rule in Japanese schools.

Hemmi made only a few lines of special purpose slide rules. For chemists there was model 257. There were also several for electrical engineering (153, 154, 255, 256) and for surveying (90A, 90B, 91A, 92, 93,94, 95, 96).

For export to Europe, Hemmi had 10 models with System Rietz. Later several models were made with System Darmstadt, which had become so important in the German-speaking countries. These were made from bamboo, and their construction was first-rate, with aluminum "springs" in the stator floors and cursors with framed glass. [81] However, German competition was strong, and Hemmi slide rules had difficulty penetrating the European markets, with the exception of Switzerland. Mainly Hemmi adopted the American example and focused on duplex models. Among them the Duplex Model 259D must be given special attention. For the engineer this slide rule had a distinct, well-balanced scale configuration, and the 259D was the most widely-sold standard model in the Hemmi duplex series. It was very successful in the U.S.

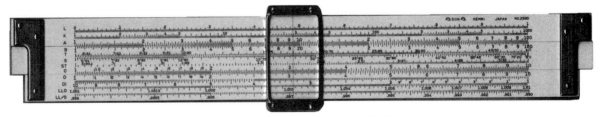

Fig.51. Sun Hemmi duplex (Model 259D)

Also noteworthy were four extra-long duplex slide rules that remained in production until the end. The Super-Precision (Model 200) is a good example of this series. This slide rule carried the concept of the extended scales to the extreme! It had 24 scale segments, each 40 cm long. With its six fixed and six sliding scale segments on each side, the "200" offered the precision that could be obtained with an effective scale length of 240 cm.

The scale ranges on the "200" are indicated below:

Front scales from top down
Back scales from top down

D6	6.8130	10.000	DF6	5.6246	8.2540
D5	4.6416	6.8130	DF5	3.8312	5.6246
D4	3.1623	4.6416	DF4	2.6102	3.8312
C6	6.8130	10.000	CF6	5.6246	8.2540
C5	4.6416	6.8130	CF5	3.8312	5.6246
C4	3.1623	4.6416	CF4	2.6102	3.8312
C3	2.1544	3.1623	CF3	1.7783	2.6102
C2	1.4678	2.1544	CF2	1.2115	1.7783
C1	1.0000	1.4678	CF1	0.8254	1.2115
D3	2.1544	3.1623	DF3	1.7783	2.6102
D2	1.4678	2.1544	DF2	1.2115	1.7783
D1	1.0000	1.4678	DF1	0.8254	1.2115

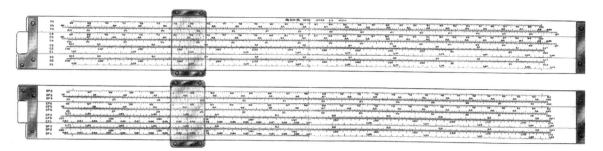

Fig.52. Sun Hemmi Super Precision (Model 200)

This slide rule is certainly a curiosity. In spite of its six pairs of scale segments on each side, the "200" offers only the two basic one-cycle scales. This slide rule would have been of use mainly in commerce and banking. On the other hand, the application of the corresponding – but folded – scales on the back offered an advantage. If a number or result on the slide was beyond the stator on one side, the number was available on the other side. Therefore it was never necessary to move the slide to the other end in order to make a setting or read a result!

Hemmi's three other extra-long slide rules had 50 cm scales:

Model 279 had the usual scale configuration for engineers but offered higher precision.

Model 275 was for electrical engineers.

Model 154 was for electrical engineers, had two cursors, plus the following:

1) arc tan h (a+jb) for electrical circuits

2) hyperbolic functions for complex numbers

3) conversion of rectangular coordinates to polar coordinates and vice versa

4) sum and difference of squares (e.g., $a^2 + b^2 - c^2$) using a cursor feature

5) trig and hyperbolic functions in one setting

6) logs for all functions (by using the hairline)

7) all scales coordinated to avoid the need to transfer settings.

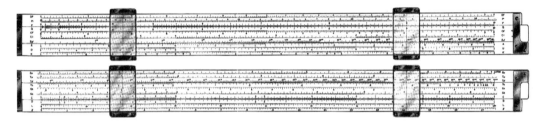

Fig.53. Sun Hemmi Elektrotecnics (Model 154)

Of course Hemmi-SUN dominated the market in Japan completely, but sales in the U.S. were also good. In 1963, "the golden year for slide rules," Hemmi reported making an astonishing one million units. However, even for Hemmi, the mid-1970s were the end of an era.

Poland

Skala Spóldzialnia Pracy, Warsaw, Poland   **SKALA**

SKALA was established in 1948 as a state-operated factory for making drafting compasses and dividers. It was formed by amalgamating small shops that were already engaged in this business. An engineer named Ciarciara joined the firm and brought with him a workshop and know-how for making rulers, straight edges, and other drafting instruments. Around this time, by order of Minister A. Wang, SKALA also tried to manufacture mechanical calculating machines. This caused great problems, and around 1956 the company abandoned its attempts to make calculating machines and began to make slide rules instead. At first SKALA made cardboard slide rules for schools, but these slide rules were of poor quality and were discontinued. In 1956 SKALA started making one-sided slide rules of pearwood (or beechwood) with celluloid scales. These slide rules were sold mainly in Poland, but also in other Eastern Block countries. The SKALA slide rules included Model SLPG (a 25 cm slide rule developed by M. Gloch and similar to the Rietz), Model SLK (12.5 cm version of SLPG), Model SLPK (25 cm, for machining time), and SLPE (a 25 cm Elektro). Later in 1970, after the company switched to injection molded slide rules of plastic, SKALA introduced Model SLPP, a "half-duplex" with the following scales: L, P, K, A/B, CI, C/D, S, T, ST.

In 1976 SKALA stopped making slide rules. It continued on as a workers' cooperative association which made compass dividers, wooden drawing boards, templates, and other drafting instruments.

Switzerland

Heinrich Daemen-Schmid, Zurich   LOGA
later Uster, Switzerland
Loga Calculator Co.

Although more than 50 Swiss slide rule makers are known, the most interesting ones were Kern & Cie and Eschmann-Wild. Both were famous for their topographic slide rules. Julius Billeter, his son Ernst and the National Company (Ernst´s brother Max) were mainly known for their cylindrical slide rules and Walter Hiltpold for semicircular ones. However, the Swiss brand Loga is the best recognized because of its cylindrical slide rules. (See Cylindrical Slide Rules.)

The firm was founded around the turn of the century by a Prussian immigrant, a textile merchant named Heinrich Daemen-Schmid. The firm was first situated in Zurich and later in Uster (a town not far from Zurich). The firm carried the founder's name until 1915, when the firm's name was changed to Loga Calculator Company.

Until the 1930s the firm was a creative and successful maker of the cylindrical slide rules that are highly valued by collectors today. However the firm also made a few straight slide rules. They had a rather original design for which Swiss patents were granted in 1916 and 1918. These slide rules were made of three layers of cardboard, the edges being protected by a metal frame. Scales were printed on both sides and the celluloid cursor was a wrap-around type. The three layers made it possible to have a separate slide on each side. Because of this feature, Loga called them "double slide rules."

Three main versions of the linear rules are known, one for technical, one for electrical, and one for commercial applications. All these linear rules were made in the rather unusual scale lengths of 15 and 30 cm. The technical version corresponds to the Rietz-system, with additional folded scales. There were eight hairlines on the back of the cursor.

The merchant type was a dual-purpose slide rule with one side for commercial calculations and the other side for common arithmetical calculations. The merchant side listed many constants (foreign currencies and non decimal weight and measure units) and a split percentage scale for interest rates up to 9%.

There was also a cheap Loga-type slide rule consisting of just a pair of loose sticks of cardboard, which slipped one along the other. Each one had two scales, a linear one from 1 to 20 and a logarithmic one two cycles from 1 to 10. These sticks were used in elementary schools to explain how a slide rule worked. The two linear scales could be used to demonstrate addition and subtraction, and the two logarithmic scales could be used to demonstrate multiplication and division.

Loga also made a "Date Finder" to determine the number of days between two calendar dates (both for 360- and 365 day-years). Finally, Loga sold blank slide rules for users who wanted to mark in their own special scales.

When the production of cylindrical slide rules came to an end in the 1930s, due to the growing success of mechanical calculating machines, Loga began to develop a line of more than 30 different circular slide rules. By the 1980s, however, the end had come for Loga.(92)

Demonstration Slide Rules

Demonstration slide rules were the most important aid for teaching the use of the slide rule. The importance of demonstration slide rules was already recognized by the end of the 1800s, and they were employed in lectures and in instruction.

All the big makers of slide rules included demonstration slide rules in their line. The majority of these demonstration slide rules were large (1m-2m) wooden rules with celluloid faces. These devices were designed to be hung over the classroom's blackboard. Later in the 1960s, along with more modern instructional methods, transparent projection slide rules (40x20cm) were added.

Today we can appreciate that demonstration slide rules profited the maker indirectly. Without doubt the use of a certain company's demonstration model obligated the instructor to have his students use the same company's hand model. This relationship was very successfully manipulated. Indeed, there was a classic example in the U.S. In the 1960s Pickett deployed its demonstration slide rules very aggressively and, as a result, overtook its major competitor (Keuffel & Esser) in the classroom market. Also, in Japan, Sun Hemmi, which was the absolute leader in the domestic slide rule market, had distributed a large number of teaching slide rules. In Germany, the three leading slide rule makers maintained their relative positions in the market by providing demonstration slide rules on very favorable terms.

It was generally true that the slide rule maker was forced to sell demonstration slide rules below cost or even donate them to a school, in order for the school to adopt the same firm's hand slide rules. However, this form of promotion paid for itself over the years. Thus the demonstration slide rule usually was a "loss leader." It was very expensive to make, and the small number needed did not yield any economies of scale. Even during the era of injection molded slide rules, demonstration slide rules were largely hand made.

Fig.54. A.W. Faber demonstration slide rule ca. 1900

Extra long slide rules were mentioned in the literature by the end of the 1800s. They were made "on order," one at a time, by skilled hand workers. According to his colleague Sedlacek, the Austrian mathematician Schulz von Straßnitzki used, in his Sunday lectures at the Polytechnical Institute in Vienna, a black board demonstration slide rule that was made to order by a Viennese mechanic named Werner. This teaching slide rule was very large (2.6 m long, 30 cm high, and 5 cm thick). It was made of maple, and the markings were made with india ink. A carrier connected three rails, in whose slots ran four movable slides. A total of 12 logarithmic slides were available. However there was no cursor, which explains why four slides were available. [96] The rule designed by Sedlacek appears to have been a unique precursor because no other slide rule of this size and type is known from this period. [97] Only after the mass production of slide rules around the turn of the century did demonstration slide rules begin to show up in catalogs.

Strangely, demonstration slide rules are rarely mentioned in American catalogs. However, judging by the specimens in the hands of collectors, the demonstration slide rules offered in the U.S. were limited to a few essential models, i.e., the Mannheim system and a few important double-sided slide rules. Pickett had the largest line of demonstration slide rules.

Beginning around 1905, the German slide rule makers offered teaching models that were made of poplar or linden wood and were 1 or 2 meters long. They carried only four scales (A/B, C/D). They had white markings on black background, and stencils were used to mark the scales. The demonstration slide rule had by this time become necessary and widely distributed, because instruction about the hand slide rule had become recommended or even required in schools. In the slide rule's "glory days" (after World War II) demonstration slide rules were of higher quality. Most were made of poplarwood with Astralon surfaces and scales that were applied by various photochemical methods. For example, in the case of Aristo-D&P, demonstration versions (1.5 and 2 meter) of the following successful models were available: Scholar models, Profi-model Studio, Studiolog, and Multilog. The double-sided demonstration slide rules had swivel mountings that permitted the side rule to be flipped upwards or downwards.

In the case of Faber-Castell, there were demonstration slide rules available for the following models: System Elektro (1m), Normal-Trig (1m), System Darmstadt (1.5m), Disponent (1.5m), the entire school slide rule series (1.5m), the Duplex (1.25m), and the Novo-Duplex (1.25m).

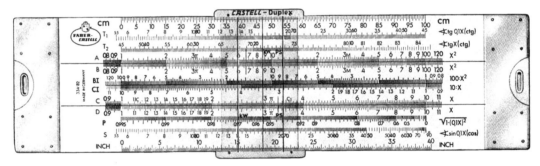

Fig.55. Faber-Castell demonstration slide rule

Nestler offered demonstration slide rules for the following models: System Rietz (1m), the school series (1m), the Polymath-Duplex (1.5m), and the Multimath-Duplex (1.5m).

In the last decades of the slide rule era, special teaching slide rules were made for overhead projectors. Typically these consisted of two sheets of transparent Plexiglass. The lower fixed sheet had the scales of the stator. The upper sliding sheet carried the scales of the slide. In the case of double-sided slide rules, the two sides were displayed above one another on the same side of the demonstration slide rule. There was a cursor that engaged in a slot along the upper edge of the projection slide rule. Aristo-D&P, Faber-Castell, and Graphoplex all offered such projection rules.

Dennert & Pape also offered another form of projection rule that designed for 35mm slide projectors. This projection rule was available for D&P's Scholar, the Bischolar, the Trilog, and the Junior models. This form of projection slide rule was very handy and very effective for projecting large images; it had the disadvantage however of having the slide projection frame serve as a "fixed cursor," requiring both the stator and slide to be moved across the frame. This was an awkward process that required some practice to master.

Today demonstration slide rules are splendid collector's pieces, and they lend a nostalgic note to many offices and rumpus rooms.

Slide Rule Literature: A User's Guide

The published material on slide rules offers a rich opportunity for the collector. This material includes some "classics," i.e., rare, old books that are only available in libraries.

Florian Cajori's famous book on the history of slide rules mentions almost 300 references, beginning in 1620 with Edmund Gunter's "Canon Triangulorum" (1620) and ending in 1909 with "Engineering News." Also, in his chapters on the early history of the slide rule in individual countries such as France, Hungary, Italy, and Germany, Cajori mentions many textbooks and their authors.

Another bibliography that was published recently [98] cites over 500 titles of references about slide rules, from the beginning of the slide rule era to the end. Some of these references are about slide rules in general; some are devoted to individual models.

In addition to these sources, there are articles that have appeared in scientific journals since 1970. These articles include over 100 titles in the "Journal of the Oughtred Society" since 1991 [99] and many articles in the "Bulletin of the Scientific Instrument Society" (England). It is impossible, in a book like this one, to describe, or even mention, all these publications. However, they have clearly made an invaluable contribution to posterity by documenting the history and the development of the slide rule.

The majority of publications about slide rules were manuals for the use and care of individual slide rules. Typically these manuals were written and published when the slide rule first came on the market. Most were very modest publications, printed in a standard size on inexpensive paper. At first these manuals were purchased separately from the related slide rule maker. As a result, for a person interested in slide rules but with limited contacts, purchasing a slide rule and a book about the slide rule could be quite a little adventure prior to 1900. In many cases only a few copies of these early slide rule manuals and books have survived, and they are prized by collectors.

Only much later did the makers format and fold the instructions so that they could be packed with the slide rule and sold as a unit. In most cases, the text of these manuals was devoted to an explanation of the scales of the relevant slide rule and to a few examples of calculations.

However, there were also guides in the form of hardcover books with good quality paper. The features of these books conformed to the tastes of the time, and these books were purchased separately. They explained most of the contemporary models, and some of these books were very thorough and had many examples.

Also, the books of pioneers, like Thompson, Pickworth, and Hammer, were especially interesting since they often included "tips" for the use of certain scales (with examples) and good advice about the latest models of the time. In most cases the authors of these books were distinguished mathematicians (e.g., professors) who were interested in making the slide rule more widely used. In most cases the books were published at the author's expense, not commissioned or financed by a slide rule maker. These books tended to be very impartial and generic, and therefore they could be used with all slide rules.

Slide rules were also mentioned briefly in special chapters in standard mathematics textbooks. This phenomenon began slowly, but it became relatively common in the golden era of the slide rule, i.e., beginning in the mid-1930s. This often happened in connection with the adoption of a new curriculum imposed by the ministry of education.

Some representative slide rule manuals and textbooks are described in more detail below.

England was the country with by far the most slide rule publications, and the majority of these appeared in the glorious two centuries after 1620. This was the time when special purpose slide rules were made by individual craftsmen, and each of these slide rules required its own set of instructions. They were usually written by the inventor (who was often also the maker), and the slide rule carried the inventor's name. The same famous names appear again here: Coggeshall, Everard, Gunter, Leybourn, Mountaine, Ward, Wingate, and others. Edmund Gunter's scale and its elaborations alone were the subject of many publications during these remarkable two centuries. As we know, in the birthplace of the slide rule, these two centuries were followed in 1850 by a big gap, when England failed to join in the development of general-purpose slide rules like the Mannheim. Not until after World War I did English slide rule manuals, textbooks, and slide rules slowly come on the market; by the end of World War II large numbers were being offered. This boom trend continued until the mid-1970s, by which time 40 new titles had appeared.

Among the representative English authors, Charles N. Pickworth deserves special attention. His collaboration on a manual with Faber-Castell has already been mentioned. Pickworth's other book *The Slide Rule; a Practical Manual* [100] was one of the best, most famous, and most successful slide rule books ever published. It went through 24 editions between 1894 and 1945. Each edition explained the slide rules that were commonly in use at the time and all the possible calculations. The book offered practical examples, and the last chapter was devoted to the newest slide rules that had just been developed. As was common with many English guides, Pickworth's book included a large appendix with measurement formulas, specific gravity, weights of materials, and other data. Anyone who had the good fortune to own all 24 editions could trace the appearance and the development of many slide rules.

In the **United States,** William Cox was well known and wrote books on the two important Keuffel & Esser slide rule lines, i.e., the Mannheim rules and the Duplex rules. His first booklet (1891) was titled *The Slide Rule for K&E* and referred to the models No. 1743 and No. 1746, both Mannheim types with brass all-metal cursors (made by D&P Altona). [101] Subsequent instruction manuals for the Mannheim types and then the Duplex slide rules appeared around 1909-1915. Other K&E authors were Allan R. Cullimore (1915), William Breckenridge(1924-1938), and M.P. Weinbach and A.F. Puchstein (1939). However, there were other authors who wrote manuals for Dietzgen (Leon Walter Rosental) and Pickett & Eckel. [101] These user guides were usually very thorough and most were of good quality.

Of course, among publications in the U.S., Florian Cajori's book *A History of the Logarithmic Slide Rule and Allied Instruments* [102] should be mentioned once again. This book is a rich source of slide rule history for the years preceding 1900. Cajori reported mainly on the history of the slide rule in Europe, and, at that time, there certainly was no single publication that offered even a fraction of the source material that he found. When Cajori published this book, he was teaching at a small college in Colorado. It is truly astounding how, from this remote place, Cajori succeeded in ascertaining so many names and dates; and this at a time when information transfer was still difficult and tedious. His book is an extraordinary piece of research, and all researchers who followed him have found their task made easier because of it.

Cajori does not attempt to instruct the reader about how to use the slide rule or to provide examples, but almost all the linear (and circular) slide rules known up to 1900 are listed in his book. In addition there is a virtually complete list of the relevant publications. However, most impressive is the detailed treatment of the history of the slide rule. Of course he could only report on the beginnings of the "new comers" in Europe and Japan, such as A.W Faber, Dennert & Pape, Nestler, and Hemmi. One can almost declare Cajori's book a "required lecture" for anyone who is interested in the history of slide rules before 1900. By reprinting Cajori's book in 1994, Astragal Press (Mendham, NJ) has done a great service to slide rule historians and provided a great tribute to the slide rule.

Another prominent example of slide rule literature from the U.S. is the textbook by J.E. Thompson. (103) He was a professor in the Department of Mathematics at the Pratt Institute in Brooklyn, U.S. and the first edition of his book appeared in 1930. He describes the most important milestones in the development of the slide rule and provides very clear examples of calculations, first using the Mannheim system and then with the duplex slide rule. He provides practical examples of interest to machinists (e.g., calculations relating to wheels, pumps, steam engines, turbines, etc.). There is a special chapter with tables and gauge points – a feature usually seen only in books from England. Also there is information about special models from K&E, including the famous (and very collectable) Charpentier circular slide rule, the Thacher, and the Fuller. This author regards Thompson's book as one of the best on slide rules.

Germany's list of slide rule books begins in 1718 with Michael Scheffelt's manual for his device. In it the author first describes how the slide rule is made from wood and then describes the following scales: Sinus, Quadr. Zoll (inches), the combined scale for Tetragonica, Area i. Zoll, Reductiones Corporum Regularium, Metall Area Globi, the individual scales for Tangens, Cubic Zoll, Dec. Zoll, Arithmetica (type A), Arithmetica (type B), and Ulmer Zoll. Scheffelt's book contains over 300 practical examples, which touch on most areas of mathematics, but the book taxes the mathematical ability of the user. [104]

Another classic is Captain Ludwig Jerrmann's *Die Gunterscale* (1888) [105], with its nautical examples. For example (Jerrmann's Example 1): "The bearing on the Arcona Lighthouse is SW 3/4 W. After sailing S 3/4 W for 21.6 miles, the new bearing is NW 1/4 W. At what distance from Arcona was each bearing made and in which direction will one see Arcona if one sailed SES 12.6 miles after the second bearing was taken?" There are also exercises in basic calculation, such as (Jerrmann's Example 8): "What is 315:37?" Jerrmann carefully explains how to solve these problems by using the Gunter scale and compass dividers. Thus Jerrmann was recommending the use of the Gunter scale as a navigational aid more than 250 years after Edmund Gunter invented it. Jerrmann wrote his book near the end of the era of great sailing ships, and who knows how many captains navigated around Cape Horn with the aid of the Gunter scale and a compass divider?

 Professor E. Hammer's book *Der logarithmische Rechenschieber und sein Gebrauch* (first published in 1897 with five subsequent editions) [106] has already been mentioned. Hammer picked up where Cajori left off. In the first chapters he called attention to the German slide rule makers, their innovations, and their special models. He discussed the conceptual advances, and cited the authors of books about slide rules. In the subsequent chapters he explained the use of slide rules.

Mass production of slide rules at Dennert & Pape marked the beginning of the "great slide rule era" in Germany. Around this same time A. Goering authored a 32 page slide rule primer (1872). [107]

In 1896, A.W. Faber started *Anleitung zum Gebrauch des Rechenstabes* (A Slide Rule Primer). A basic model (No. 360, corresponding to System Mannheim) was described, using the scale configuration A/B, C/D//S, L, T. In addition the primer included 13 diagrams which showed in great detail the exact scale positions for solving several sample problems. [108]

A more recent and very good German textbook is Albert Rohrberg's *Der Rechenstab im Unterricht aller Schularten* (Slide rule instruction in schools of all kinds). This book went through several editions in the 1920s. It included many practical examples, some unusual applications like addition and subtraction, and even a section on the slide rule and the musical scale. The final chapter, on the history of slide rules, is also worth mentioning. [109]

Vom Abakus zum Rechenschieber by Max Hartmuth [110] is a very richly illustrated book. It begins with number concepts, numbers, calculations. It continues with number tables from ancient Greece, the abacus in the early middle ages, logarithms, and Edmund Gunter. There follows a successful introduction to the use of the slide rule, with over 200 very interesting practical examples, some of which are illustrated with drawings. Because of these drawings (many of which were original) and the well-explained examples, the book was highly respected in its time. There is no known picture of Edmund Gunter, but this book's artist has imagined how the Gunter scale came to be.

During the 1950s and 1960s, the two German slide rule makers, Artisto-Dennert & Pape and A.W. Faber-Castell, both published small slide rule magazines which were available free of charge to interested parties. The *Aristo-Mitteilungen* (Editor Rolf Jäger) and Faber-Castell's *Rechenstab-Briefe* (Editor Harald Bachmann) contained contributions from many slide rule users, including engineers, teachers, and, most importantly, academics from schools of engineering. These magazines were published up to the end of the slide rule era and were extremely popular.

An enumeration of further publications would exceed the scope of this book. Also, the very large number of foreign language slide rule books cannot be covered here.

Collecting Slide Rules

Collecting slide rules has become a fascinating hobby for more and more people, resulting in an increase in the desirability and thus price of collectible slide rules. If one were to compare slide rule collecting with stamp collecting, the Gunter scale would be analogous in a historical sense to the Blue Mauritius. (Of course the Blue Mauritius is far more rare and valuable, and relatively recent versions of the Gunter scale can still be found at English flea markets.)

Close behind the Gunter scale in rarity and value would be the English slide rules that are diligently listed in the publications of Baxandall and Cajori. Many of these rules are very rare. They include the slide rules of Bissaker, Everard, the Soho-rules, the rules of Silvanus Bevan, and the rules known for their able makers, such as Dring & Fage, W. & S. Jones, Rooker, Bate, Cary, and John Davis & Son. Of course there are the excellent models made by the French firm Tavernier-Gravet.

However, collecting the slide rules produced during the last century by the large makers mentioned in this book is likely to be a more successful undertaking. It is still possible to find early models in this category, those made before World War I and those made during the 1920s and 1930s. Some of the latter could also qualify as rarities. There are large numbers of the mass-produced, common slide rules like the System Rietz, Darmsadt, and Elektro in Europe, as well as the various duplex models made in Europe and elsewhere. Of course, some of the American duplex slide rules go back to the beginning of the 1900s, and these slide rules are very desirable. Special purpose slide rules of various kinds can be extremely rare since, because of their limited market, they were produced in relatively small numbers. Slide rule/Addiator combinations, like the one that Faber-Castell offered, and slide rule/pocket calculator combinations are also relatively rare.

In summary it can be said that slide rules from the period before World War I don't turn up very often at all. Those next most difficult to find are the slide rules made between World War I and 1945. Slide rules made after 1945 are easier to find; they were made in so many varieties, however, that it is difficult to assemble complete series.

It should be mentioned that there are already two organizations for slide rule collectors. The Oughtred Society was formed in 1991 and is based in the U.S. It began with 11 members and now has a worldwide membership of over 400 collectors and dealers. The Oughtred Society sponsors a journal which appears twice each year. The *Journal* publishes interesting articles about old and special models, profiles of slide rule makers (especially American firms), historical data, etc. The Oughtred Society organizes meetings in the U.S. for collectors, and supports meetings in Europe.

A second, smaller, but very active organization, called KRING, is based in Holland. KRING has produced a comprehensive "Blue Book" that describes and codes all the linear, circular, and cylindrical slide rules in the possession of its members. This listing already includes all the famous makers and models. The listing is continuously updated.

References and Additional Notes

[1] The great English philosopher and historian David Hume (1711-1776) said of Napier: "The person to whom the title of a great man is more justly due than to any other whom the country ever produced." Sometimes Napier was compared with Archimedes because of his secret inventions for the defense of the island, e.g., focusing mirrors to light hostile ships, a cannon and a battle-car of metal. (Rudolf W. Lauri, "Napier and Jost Bürgi," 1927).

[2] Jost Bürgi was the most important maker of watches and astronomical instruments of the Renaissance, as well as an astronomer and mathematician. From 1579 he was member of the observatory in Kassel, founded by the Hessian Landgraf Wilhelm IV, an engaged astronomer, as well. An ingenious inventor and mechanician, Bürgi constructed very precise and ornamented watches, instruments, globes and celestial automatic machines. He spent the years 1604-1620 at the Imperial court in Prague (German Emperor Rudolf II) . There he also met Johannes Kepler, to whom Bürgi explained the logarithms that he had started in Kassel in 1588. Kepler advised him to publish his system, but it was too late (1620). (Bibl. 21-Mac). Bürgi named his Tables "Progress-Tabulen"; they had (in red) the logarithms as number of entry and (black) the numeri. It was a table of antilogarithms. (Bürgi´s logarithms were founded on the base of 1,0001, Napier´s on the base of 0.999 and Briggs´on the base of 10, the so called "common logarithms.")

[3] There exists a famous report about their first meeting by an astrologer William Lilly in his *History of his Life and Times*: "When the great mathematicians met, almost one quarter of an hour was spent, each beholding other almost with admiration, before one word was spoke. At last Mr. Briggs began: 'My Lord, I have undertaken this journey purposely to see your person, and to know what engine of wit or ingenuity you came first to think of this most excellent help unto astronomy, viz. the logarithms, but my Lord, being by you found out, I wonder nobody else found it out before, when now known it is so easy.' " (Bibl. 34, Briggs, p.1234)

[4] These complements to Briggs' "Chilias" appeared in Brigg's most famous work, *Arithmetica Logarithmica*. (Bibl.34, Briggs p.1234).

[5] Bibl. 34, Gunter, p.793.

[6] The sector (Proportionalzirkel or compas de proportion first designed by Galilei) was a forerunner of the slide rule and was used from its invention at the beginning of the 17th century until the midth of the 19th century. It was used for the calculation of natural numbers, squares, cubes, and so on. Problems involving multiplication and division were solved "mechanically" based on the proportion. The two legs of the compasslike instrument were graduated in equal parts, numbered 1,2,3,4,5, and so on. For example, to multiply 35 by 16, one took by a divider the distance 35 on one leg, then opened at 10 the sector by this distance. Then at 16 to 16 the opening was calipered. At last this distance was fixed by the divider on one leg and gave the result.

[7] Bibl. 29- Rohr, p.137-138.

[8] Bibl. 7-Den, p.50.

[9] Benjamin Donn (also Donne) (1729 – 1798), mathematician, published some books about mathematics, a lot of maps of western England, and some charts of the western ocean, but he also designed mathematical instruments, a list of which will be found in the "Mathematical Tables, or Tables of Logarithms." (Bibl. 34, Donn, p.1126).

[10] Bibl.18-Jerr, p.1-27.

[11] Bibl. 2-Ar-Jag, p.1-2 (transl. *An Appreciation of the History of the Slide Rule*).

[12] Bibl. 34, Oughtred , p.1250.

[13] Oughtred's book was translated into English and made available for the public benefit by Willam Forster, London, 1632. (Forster was a pupil of Oughtred and afterwards taught mathematics.) Although the book itself describes only the "circle of proportion," the dedication of this book briefly mentions that Oughtred also used linear scales which were set against each other. These could be used without relying on compass dividers. A supplement to this book was published in 1632. The supplement contained an appendix titled, "The declaration of the two rulers for calculation." (See Bibl13-Ham, p.5).

[13A] William Leybourn (1626-1700?) was a teacher of mathematics and a professional land surveyor in London. He was a successful author and editor of Edmund Gunter´s works. He also published (1667) *The Line of Proportion or (of) Numbers, commonly called Gunter´s Line, made easie, a treatise on the sliding-rule* and, until 1677, he published the *Works* of Edmund Gunter. There were several further titles. For example in 1690 he published his *Cursus Mathematicus, Mathematical Sciences in Nine Books*, a folio volume of over 900 pages, including the substance of his former publications. Leybourn´s works all grew out of his teaching and were deservedly popular. They are clear and attractive in style , and they are the work of a man of considerable ingenuity and uncommon industry. (Bibl.34, Leybourn p.1088).

[14] Augustus de Morgan (1806 – 1871) was a mathematician and energetic worker, whose energy was chiefly absorbed by his voluminous writings upon mathematical, philosophical, and antiquarian points. In 1828, he became the first professor of mathematics of the just started University of London. There was a break from 1831 to 1836; then he was reappointed and remained professor for the next thirty years. (Bibl. 34E, de Morgan p.781-783). Also well-known is his library, consisting, by the end of his life, of about 3000 volumes. The library enabled him to turn his bibliographical researches to good account in his writings (Bibl. 34, de Morgan p.783). Hammer speaks of de Morgan "als bibliographisch unvergleichlich bewandert" (bibliographically it is incomparably proficient), and Hammer refers to de Morgan´s article "Slide Rule" in the *English Cyclopaedia*,1842 (Bibl. 6.).

[15] Bibl.1-All, p.2.

[16] Richard Delamaine was a mathematician and pupil of Oughtred. Delamaine's earliest work *Grammalogia, or the Mathematicall Ring, extracted from the Logarythms and projected circle* (1631) was attacked in Oughtred's *Circles of Proportion*. (See Bibl. 34, Delamaine, p.751.)

[17] In his *History of Gunter´s Scale and Slide Rule* (Bibl.5-Caj, see III and IV), Florian Cajori included a long examination of Delamaine´s *Grammelogia* (III); and in his *Controversy* (IV) a discussion of Oughtred on the invention of the circular slide rule. It was a long and hostile dispute between a professor (Oughtred) and his pupil, but at the end Cajori very wisely states: "There is always danger that rival claimants of an invention or discovery will proceed on assumption that no one else could possibly have come independently upon the same devices that they themselves did; the history of science proves the opposite. Seldom is an invention of any note made by only one man. We do not feel competent to judge Delamaine´s case. We know too little about him as a man. We incline to the opinion that the hypothesis on independent invention is the most plausible." At any rate, Delamaine figures in the history of the slide rule as the publisher of the earliest book thereon and as an enthusiastic and skillful designer of slide rules (Bibl.5-Caj,p.159).

The following are two examples from the collection at the Science Museum in London:

1. "Early slide rule" from 1742, approximately 90 cm long, for carpenters, square (in cross section), with one slide, scales A, B, and C, various additional inch scales plus special scales for calculations related to wood.

2. "Slide Rule" made by J. Stutchbury in the mid 18th century, box wood, approximately 40 cm long, with 2 slides, with square, SS, and SL scales. [18]

[18] Scales SS and SL were used to find the ullage of a cask with axis horizontal (SL segments lying) and axis vertical (SS segments standing). Bibl.5-Caj, p.19. Ullage is the unused capacity of a container, i.e., the portion remaining to be filled.

[19] James Watt was originally a mathematical instrument maker (sic) and also a workman of great delicacy of touch. In 1755 he found his first employment in London as a slide rule maker, under John Morgan, of Finch Lane, Cornhill. At that time Watt wrote the following to his father (an instrument maker) about Morgan: "Though he works chiefly in the brass way, yet he can teach me most branches of the business, such as rules, scales, quadrants etc." Less than two months after Watt's arrival in London, he reported that he had made a brass parallel rule eighteen inches long, "and a brass scale of the same length." Watt, however, having doubtless acquired proficiency in the art of rule making did not "work for himself," as it appears he intended to do, but turned his intention to the improvement of the steam engine, and thus conferred greater benefits upon the world than he would have had he continued to manufacture "parallel rules." (*Measuring Rules* by J. Rabone, Jun. (Bibl.28-Rob). Mr. Rabone writes (1866): "It may be interesting to know that the sliding rule, long used by James Watt, is still preserved in the possession of an eminent founder, and is still used as a check in testing calculations. Is it not probable that this rule may be the handiwork of its former great possessor?"(Bibl.28-Rob.).

[20] Bibl. 7-Den, p.54.

[21] Bibl. 41-Zol. This is one of the best and most detailed reports about Soho slide rules.

[22] Bibl. 37-Tho, p.7. Thompson mentions further: "This is the first recorded use of what is now known as a runner or cursor. In discussing Newton´s work, this device was made more definite and described as a "marking line moving parallel to itself" by E. Stone in 1726.

[23] John Robertson (1712 – 1776), mathematician, was at last appointed clerk and librarian of the Royal Society. Besides his chief publication *The Elements of Navigation* he also wrote *Mathematical Instruments*, *On Logarithmic Tangents* and *On Logarithmic Lines on Gunter´s Scale*. (Bibl. 34, Robertson, p.1299 and Bibl.37 –Tho, p.7).

[24] William Nicholson was a great man of science, with knowledge in many fields. He wrote about natural history, chemistry, history of India. He also wrote a communication to the Royal society regarding "The Principles and Illustration of an advantageous Method of arranging the Differences of Logarithms, on Lines graduated for the purpose of Computation." Here he described a rule of ten parallel lines, equivalent to a double line of numbers upwards of twenty feet in length . (Bibl.34, Nicholson p.473-475)

[25] In Rozé's book he acknowledges that Professor Tscherepaschinski was the inventor of this scale arrangement. However, Rozé also mentions that Professor Beghin introduced this scale arrangement without knowledge of Professor Tscherepaschinski's invention. This was the origin of System Beghin. (Bibl.29A-Roz.p.2-3, Preamble).

[26] Bibl.5-Caj,p.61-62 and Bibl.34-Tho,p.17-18.

[27] Bibl. 31-Schef.

[28]. Bibl.20A-Lamb, translated *Description and Use of the Logarithmic Slide Rule for the Solution of all Calculations related to Proportions as well as Plane and Spherical Trigonometry and countless Mathematical Tables – An improvement of Scheffelt's Pes Mechanicus and Biler's Universal Instrument.* The book was printed in 1761 in Augsburg.

[29] Bibl. 5-Caj, p.53.

[30] Bibl.-33 Sel.

[31] The teaching aid is described in his book *Über Visier- und Recheninstrumente* (Concerning Sighting and Calculating Instruments) Vienna, 1856. See also Bibl. 29-Rohr, p.141-142.

[32] von Ott writes on the same page: "Especially they *(i.e., the slide rules)* can be used by every technician, for whom they are the non plus ultra of all calculating machines and an inexhaustible fount, for the slide rule can be named really founded as the golden or magic wand of the technician." (Bibl. 25-Ott, p.67).

[33] The "Dinglers Polytechnisches Journal" was founded and edited from 1820 by Johann Gottfried Dingler (1778-1855), technologist and later owner of a chemical factory. He was followed by his son Emil Maximilian, who edited the Journal from 1840 to 1874 with outstanding success in promoting industrial development in Germany.

[34] Bibl. 13-Ham.

[35] Bibl.22-Mehm.

[36] Bibl. 29-Roh.r

[37] Bibl. 16-.Hopp.272-280.

[38] Bibl. 24 – Otn.

[39] Bibl. 5-Caj, p.65, footnote 1; and Bibl.Rohr, p.140.

[40] Bibl.4-Bax, p.37 (no.136).

[41] Bibl. 4-Bax, p.31(No.93).

[42] Bibl.4-Bax, p.36 (No.127).

[43] Bibl.37-Tho. p.13 and Bibl.1-All, p.3-.

[44] The same method of scale dividing was used by the English A.G. Thornton works in Manchester after 1947. It was the result of a visit of the British Intelligence Committee (seven engineers in 1947), the purpose of which was described as follows: "The object of this investigation was to enable the British manufacturers of drawing instruments, slide rules and scales, to study the methods and conditions of the manufacture of these instruments in Germany. . . Special interest was given, when planning the trip, to concentrate on the methods of manufacture of the better quality instruments." Faber-Castell, Nestler, and Dennert & Pape were visited. The report about Faber-Castell master dies says: "The construction of the dies used in this process are of special interest and are made in the following manner." (Here follows a description which conforms to the description provided in this book.) "This method appears to be very efficient, and could well be recommended to the English manufacturer." (sic) (Bibl. 20- Kno- p. 33 - 35) . A.G. Thornton adopted this method of scale dividing.

[45] Personal communication, Rodger Shepherd.

[46] Sometimes called the Biplex in all Spanish-speaking countries because that name was registered there for K&E (the author).

[47] Thomas Everard was a mechanic and scientist. His well-known slide rule was invented in 1683. (Bibl.5-Caj, p.17-19). It became a standard type, constructed with various modifications by

most of the mathematical instrument makers from the latter part of the 17th century to the end of the 18th century. Many thousands were sold during the period 1683 to 1705. (Bibl. 4-Bax, p.27).

[48] (Bibl. 37-Tho. p.7) Dr. William Hyde Wollaston (1766 – 1822), physicist and chemist.

[49] The first slot with index marks is found on Mannheim slide rules of Gravet-Lenoir ca. 1850 (the author).

[50] Roget first and foremost was active as a physician and most of his professional life was dedicated to his lectures about psychology, medicinal themes, and activities. His great invention of the log-log scales was just a by-product of this ingenious man's professional activities. (the author).

[51] see VDI – Zeitschrift 1901 p. 720, with letters of Blanc and Schweth; also Bibl. 26/5-She,p.31 and Bibl.26/6-Kug,p.12.

[52] Bibl.2-Jag,p.7.

[53] Bibl.34-Tho., p.9.

[54] Bibl. 5-Caj, p.35.

[55] Bibl. 5-Caj, p.69.

[56] For more about Long-Scale Slide Rules see Bibl 26/9-Cha, pp. 24-34.

[57] See also Bibl. 26/1-Shep, p.6-7 and p.18.

[58] Bibl. 4-Bax, p.34 (No.109).

[59] Bibl. 33-Strub, p.778.

[60] Bibl. 15-Har, p.72.

[61] Bibl. 27-Pick, p.96ff.

[62] Bibl. 26/2-Otn, pp.21-24.

[63] Bibl. 26/3-Feel-Schu, p.33-40.

[64] Bibl. 26/4-Feel-Schu, pp.33-40, and 26/7-Feel, pp.25-29. See also Shep-p.30.

[65] Bibl.19-Joss, pp.49-57.

[66] See also Bibl. 37-Tho, pp.217-219.

[67] Bibl.14-Ham, pp.433-441.

[68] Feely, Wayne E.;"Thacher Cylindrical Slide Rules," *Chronicle* of Early American Industries Association, vol. 50, no.4, p.125-127 (Not mentioned in Bibliography).

[69] Bibl.37-Tho, pp.218-220.

[70] Information about Otis-King types and models is still evolving. For references to this dynamic literature see JOS vol 7, no 1, pp.33-37, 1998.

[71] Extensive lists of slide rule makers are to be found in Bibl. 17-hop.

[72] Bruce Babcock, Dietzgen Catalog Matrix, included as part of the Journal of the Oughtred Society for October1996, Volume 5, No. 2.

[73] the author, personal communication with John F. Knott.

[74] For more about Thornton, see also Bibl.26/8-Knot, pp.29-31.

[75] Bibl.35-Snod, p.157.

[76] For more about UNIQUE see also Bibl.26/8-Hop, Bar, Knot, p.32-44

[77] Bibl.27-Pick.

[78] Lothar von Faber´s granddaughter Ottilie, his sole heiress, married Count Castell-Rüdenhausen in 1898 and got permission from Prinzregent Luitpold to adopt the name Countess

Faber-Castell. After that time the brand name Faber-Castell was applied first to lead pencils (1905) and later (c. 1913) to slide rules. (the author)

[79] Model 1/48 was made of wood. After 1950 it was succeeded by the plastic model 111/48.

[80] See Figure 10.

[81] For example, an excellent Darmstadt type was the No. 130.

[82] Personal letter to the author.

[83] Bibl.42-Züh, pp.198-199.

[84] Catalog K&E 1, 1890 and Bibl. 26/2, pp.12-13, A Pioneering K&E Engineer.

[85] Personal communication, Rodger Shepherd.

[86] A guide for estimating the age of K&E slide rules 1887-1955, compiled by Bruce Babcock, PhD. with assistance from Robert Otnes, Rodger Shepherd, and Henry Aldinger. Privately published by Bruce Babcock, April 16, 1992.

[87] Personal communication, Wayne E. Feely to Rodger Shepherd.

[88] Bibl. 26/2 Otn, p.4.

[89] Bibl.10-Feel, pp.62-67

[90] POST had entered into a joint venture with the Japanese slide rule maker SUN-Hemmi. This served to bring these outstanding bamboo slide rules into the American market.

[91] For more about Keuffel & Esser see also Bibl. 24 - Otn; (not mentioned in the Bibliography) Oughtred Society Journal Vol.2, No.1,1993, pp.4 –14; (excerpts of the W.L.E. Keuffel review *The First Quarter Century of My Life*); OSJ Vol. 4, number 2, 1995, (Otnes) pp.14-15, "A Page from the 1883 Keuffel & Esser Catalog;" (Morris) pp.18-24, "Model Designations of Modern Era K&E Slide Rules;" (Babcock) p.41-49, "K&E Student´s and Beginner´s Slide Rules - 1897 to 1954."

[92] Heinz Joss to the author.

[93] See also [25].

[94] Bibl. 26/1-Shep, pp.6-7 and p.18.

[95] Bibl. 26/9-Rei, p.11.

[96] Bibl.29-Rohr, 141-142.

[97] R. Mehmke (Bibl.22 in *Rechenschieber in Deutschland*) also mentions Tavernier-Gravet´s *Règles pour demonstration* with 2m length from a time in the middle of the 1800s.

[98] Bibl.-Hop, pp.257-269.

[99] See Bibl.26/ Oughtred Society Journal, several editions.

[100] Bibl. 27-Pick.

[101] Bibl. 26/8-Otn.pp.18-19. Robert Otnes, the expert author of more than 50 articles about slide rules, writes about this book by Cox: "It is somewhat ironic that this slide rule was based on a French design (Mannheim), improved and built by a German company (D&P), had its manual written by an Englishman (Cox), and became an American staple item."

[102] Bibl. 5-Caj-Reprint of the Astragal Press.

[103] Bibl. 37-Tho.

[104] Bibl. 31-Schef.

[105] Bibl. 18-Jerr.

[106] Bibl. 17-Ham.

[107] Bibl.12-Goe.

[108] Bibl. 9-Fab, 1st ed., 1896, through 8th ed., 1919.

[109] Bibl. 29-Rohr.

[110] Bibl. 15-Har.

Bibliography
(List of works consulted)

1. Allan, R.K., *Systematic Slide Rule Technique*, London, 1962 , Sir Isaac & Sons Ltd.

2. Aristo-Mitteilungen, *Eine Wertung der Geschichte des Rechenstabes*, 6/1963. (Rolf Jäger) Hamburg.

3. Balogh, Arthur, *A logarlec*, Budapest, 1970.

4. Baxandall, David, *Catalogue of the Collections in the Science Museum, Mathematics I, Calculating Machines and Instruments*, London, 1926.

5. Cajori, Florian, *The History of the Logarithmic Slide Rule and Allied Instruments and on the History of Gunter´s Scale and the Slide Rule*, Reprint 1994, Astragal Press, Mendham N.J., U.S.*

6. de Morgan, Augustus, *Penny Cyclopaedia*, Slide (or sliding) rule, 1842.

7. Dennert & Pape, *100 Jahre Dennert & Pape*, Aristo-Werke, Hamburg-Altona, 1962.

8. Dyck, Walther von, *Katalog mathematischer und mathematisch-physikalischer Modelle, Apparate und Instrumente*, Kgl.Hofdruckerei Wolf & Sohn, 1892.

9. Faber, A.W., *Anleitung zum Gebrauch des Rechenstabes*, Stein bei Nürnberg, 1901.

10. Feely, Wayne, "The last days of K&E slide rules," *Chronicle* of the Early American Industries Association, Vol. 52 No.2, June 1999.

11. Fürle, Herrmann, *Zur Theorie der Rechenschieber*, Berlin 1899, R. Gärtner´s Verlagsbuchhandlung.

12. Goering, A., *Der Rechenschieber aus dem Mechanisch-mathematischen Institut von Dennert&Pape*, Altona, 1873.

13. Hammer, Ernst, *Der logarithmische Rechenschieber und sein Gebrauch*, 5. Auflage 1918, J.B.Metzler, Stuttgart.

14. Hammer, Ernst, *Über einige neue Formen des log. Rechenschiebers, Zeitschrift für Vermessungswesen*, Band XX, Heft 16,1891.

15. Hartmuth, Max, *Vom Abakus zum Rechenschieber*, Verl. Boysen&Maasch, Hamburg 1942.

16. Hill, H. Justin, *A Course of the Slide Rules and Logarithms*, U.S. 1943.

17. Hopp, Peter, *Slide Rules, Their History, Models and Makers*, 1999, Astragal Press, Mendham N.J., U.S. *

18. Jerrmann, Ludwig, *Die Gunterscale. Vollständige Erklärung der Gunterlinien und Nachweis ihrer Entstehung nebst zahlreichen Beispielen für praktischen Gebrauch*, Eckardt & Messtorf, Hamburg 1888.

19. Joss, Heinz, 4th International Meeting Slide Rule ´98, Proceedings. **

20. Knott, John V., "Proceedings of the Fifth International Meeting of Slide Rule Collectors, Aug. 1999," (proceeding German Slide Rule Manufacture in 1946) ***

20A. Lambert, Johann Heinrich, "Beschreibung und Gebrauch der logarithmischen Rechenstäbe in Auflösung aller zur Proportion, gemeinen und sphärischen Trigonometrie gehörigen Rechnungen und in Vorstellung unzähliger mathematischer Tabellen als eine Verbesserung des Scheffeltschen Pes Mechanicus und des Bilerschen Universalinstruments," Augsburg, 1761, bei Eberhard Kletts sel. Wittib.

21. Mackensen, L. von, *Die erste Sternwarte Europas mit ihren Instrumenten und Uhren, 400 Jahre Jost Bürgi in Kassel*, Callwey-Verlag, München 1979

22. Mehmke, Rudolf, *Der Rechenschieber in Deutschland , und Soho Rules , aus Zeitschrift für Mathematik und Physik,* 49. Band, 1901

23. Nelting, R., *Der Nautisch-Astronomische und Universal-Rechenschieber und seine Verwendung,* Altona-Hamburg, 1912

24. Otnes Robert K., "Keuffel & Esser Slide Rules," Historische Bürowelt Nr. 24, 1989 and Historische Bürowelt Nr. 25, 1989

25. Ott, Karl von, *Der logarithmische Rechenschieber: Theorie und Gebrauch desselben,* Prag 1891

26. Oughtred Society, Journal of the Oughtred Society ****, several editions:

    26/1. Vol.1, No. 1, 1992 Shepherd, Rodger, Pickett Metal Slide Rules, pp. 5-8 and Pickett´s "Eye Saver Yellow," p. 18.

    26/2. Vol.2, No.1, 1993, Otnes Robert K., The Keuffel & Esser Issue, p. 4 and Thacher Notes, pp. 21-24, also Thacher Sightings p. 24.

    26/3. Vol.3, No.2, 1994, Feely, Wayne and Schure, Conrad, "Thacher Slide Rule Production," pp. 38-42.

    26/4. Vol.4, No.1, 1995, Feely, Wayne and Schure, Conrad, "The Fuller Calculating Instrument," pp. 33-40.

    26/5. Vol.4, No.2, 1995, Shepherd, Rodger, "Translation of an Article on F. Blanc´s Slide Rule," pp.31-32.

    26/6. Vol.5, No.1, 1996, Kugel, Günter, "Log-Log Slide Rule of Blanc-Contin.," pp.12-13.

    26/7. Vol.5, No.1, 1996, Feely, Wayne, "Update of Known Fuller and Thacher Rules," pp.25-29; and Shepherd, Rodger, "Comment on the Fuller Listings," p. 30.

    26/8 Vol.6, No.1, 1997, Otnes, Robert K., "K&E Instruction Manuals," pp. 18-19; and Knott, John V., "British Thornton-A Slide Rule Manufacturer of Manchester England," pp. 29-31; and Hopp, Peter, Barnes, Colin, Knott John V., "UNIQUE Slide Rules," pp. 32-44.

    26/9 Vol.8, No.1, 1999, Reichelt, Bruce, "Pickett & Eckel Slide Rule Time Line," p.11; and Chamberlain, Edwin J., "Long-Scale Slide Rules," pp.24-34.

27. Pickworth, C.N., *The Slide Rule: A Practical Manual* (1894)18th ed., Revised and partly rewritten, London 1927.

28. Roberts, Kenneth D., Reprint of John Rabone & Sons 1892 Catalogue of Rules, Tapes, Spirit Levels etc., Hockley Abbey Works, Birmingham, England, The Astragal Press, Mendham, NJ,

29. Rohrberg, Albert, *Der Rechenstab im Unterricht aller Schularten.* Eine methodische Anleitung, R. Oldenbourg, Berlin und München 1928.

29A. Rozé, P., *Théorie et Usage de la Règle à calculs*, Gauthier-Villars, Paris, 1907

30. Rudowski Werner, Begleitheft, "Rechenschieber-Ausstellung Sparkasse Bochum," Nov. 1991.

31. Scheffelt, Michael, *Pes mechanicus artificalis, oder:Neu erfundener Maß-Stab*, Ulm 1718.

32. Schuitema , Ijzebrand, "4 Artikel über Rechenschieber in Historische Bürowelt" Nr. 29, Sept. 1990.

33. Sella, Quintinio, *Teorica e pratica de regolo calcolatore*, Torino 1859

34. Smith, George, *The Dictionary of National Biography*, Founded by George Smith (23 vols.), published since 1917 by Oxford University Press, London, Geoffrey Camberledge.

35. Snodgrass, Burns, *Teach Yourself The Slide Rule,* 1958, The English University Press Ltd., London EC1.

36. Strubecker, Karl, *Einführung in die Höhere Mathematik*, Bd.I, Grundlagen, 2. verbess. Auflage, R. Oldenbourg,München, Wien 1966.

37. Thompson, J.E., *The Standard Manual of the Slide Rule, its History,Principle and Operation*, second printing, D.van Nostrand Co., Inc, New York, 1931.

38. VDI-Zeitschrift, *Zuschriften an die Redaktion*, (Blanc, Schweth), Jahrgang 45, Nr.1.

39. Wichmann Gebr., "Hauptkatalog 20," Ausgabe, appr.1935.

40. Zerfowski, Detlev, *Mechanical Calculating Machines and Calculating Tools in the Past*, (sliding rules, scales, calculating tables), A Bibliography, 1999. *****

41. Zoller, Paul, "The Soho Slide Rule: Genesis and Archaelogy," Bulletin of the Scientific Instrument Society, Nr. 57, 1998.

42. Zühlke, Marcel, *Wirtschaftlich Rechnen, Nomographie, Rechentafeln und Sonderrechenstäbe*, G. Westermann Verlag, 3. Aufl. , 1952

* Available, The Astragal Press, 5 Cold Hill Road, Suite 12, PO Box 239, Mendham NJ 07945-0239.

** Available, Heinz Joss, Rainring 4, CH 8108 Dällikon-Switzerland.

*** Available, Colin A. Barnes, 189 Mildenhall Road, Fordham, Ely,Cambs.,CB7 5NW, GB.

**** All Volumes available, The Oughtred Society, Secretary, PO Box 99077, Emeryville, California 94662.

***** Available, Detlev Zerfowski, Nordhaldenstr.5, D 71384, Weinstadt-Beutelsbach, Germany.

Appendix I
German Registered Designs and Patents Relating to Slide Rules

Registered Designs (DRGM and DBGM) Related to the Slide Rules
(Compiled with assistance from Günter Kugel and Hans Dennert)

Year	DRGM	Applicant	Claim briefly described
1894	25025	D&P	Cursor with lens fixed in frame
1895	37191	D&P	Slide rule with slotted floor
1893-4	41294	Nestler	Flexible sheet of metal
1901	148526	W. Schweth	Exponential slide rule
1901	164885	Nestler	Nickel silver screws to secure laminated celluloid
1902	173095	D&P	Slide rule of Dr. Frank
1902	181110	M. Rietz	Cubic slide rule system of Rietz
1902	192052	D&P	Adjustment screws at the side
1902	192462	Nestler	Slide rule system of Nestle
1905	247514	AW Faber	Slide rule with index edge at end of slide
1906	271169	AW Faber	Cursor with flanges that engage in the sides of the slide rule
1906	272915	Nestler	Slide rule "FIX", mahogany
1907	296340	AW Faber	Springy laminated floor
1907	306107	AW Faber	Slide rule with spring laminated into floor
1908	334146	Nestler	Slide rule Electro 32
1908	344576	AW Faber	Slide rule with Schumacher system
1908	354529	D&P	Slide rule with reciprocal divisions/scales
1908	356144	R. Nelting	The nautical slide rule
1908-9	371189	AW Faber	Slide rule with the Pickworth system
1908-9	371190	AW Faber	Wooden pegs to secure laminated celluloid
1909	383627	D&P	First "frameless" or "clearview" cursor
1909	400076 +17285	Nestler	Framed cursor with larger field
1909	400077	Hans H. Peter	Slide rule with two exponential scales on the stator
1909	400027	Nestler	Cursor
1909	400289	AW Faber	Cursor with second "periscoping" magnifying lens
1909	405280	Nestler	Slide rule with Hanauer system
1910	409844	Nestler	Chemist's slide rule

1910	437942	D&P	Slide rule with interrupted scale markings
1910	440832	D&P	Cursor of glass and celluloid
1911	452965	AW Faber	Two-part frame/housing for slide rules, with laminated steel floor attached to the two parts of the slide rule
1911	467488	Koch, H&H	Slide rule (Koch, Huxhold & Hannemann)
1911	484264	D&P	Transparent cursor with half-cylinder magnifying lens.
1912	494756	Nestler	Slide rule with articulated attached guidepieces
1912	495319	D&P	Dennert's "freeview" cursor
1912	522689	AW Faber	Springy laminated floor (or back)
1912	527555	AW Faber	Slide rule for the calculation of barometrically determined differences in altitude (Hohenner)
1913	564729	Nestler	Slide rule with scales for calculating interest and currency conversion
1914	595894	D&P	Cursor made of a flat piece of glass with two guides and retaining clips made of metal.
1914	620038	D&P	Magnifying lens mounting for cursor
1914	620039	D&P	Magnifying lens mounting for cursor
1920	767267	D&P	Cursor with celluloid end-pieces
1920	773529	AW Faber	The machine time slide rule, system of Dr. Winkel
1921	818274	D&P	Machine time slide rule, System Kresta
1923	836352	AW Faber	Columbus slide rule, System Rohrberg
1924	879342	AW Faber	The Electro 378, a slide rule for electrical and mechanical engineers.
1924	879352	AW Faber	Slide rule for foresters and lumber dealers
1924	879365	AW Faber	The Electro 378, a slide rule for electrical and mechanical engineers.
1924	879366	AW Faber	The Electro 378, with scale for voltage drop
1924	879591	AW Faber	Slide rule for lumber dealers
1924	881498	AW Faber	Slide rule for foresters
1924	881735	AW Faber	Slide rule with scales for electrical resistance and power load
1924	885425	D&P	Cursor with celluloid lens
1924	889218	Torda	Slide rule for reinforced concrete (System Torda)
1924	889460	Nestler	Slide rule with extended scales
1924	913064	D&P	Slide rule for x-ray absorption
1926	946726	D&P	"Frameless" cursor with glass notched for attachment with screws

1926	957122	D&P	Slide rule with flat grid (Gitterfeder) as the springy element
1926	969974	D&P	"Frameless" cursor with transparent attachment
1928	1038209	D&P	Slide rule with plastic base
1928	1054085	D&P	Cursor with protection against scratching.
1932	1225645	D&P	Slide rule with special metal frame.
1933	1281585	D&P	Slide rule for mathematical calculations
1933	1281686	AW Faber	Slide rule with metal reinforcement
1934	1289083	AW Faber	Pocket slide rule
1934	1296982	D&P	Slide rule or its parts made of flexible glass
1934	1314631	AW Faber	Two-sided slide rule with markings that correspond on both sides
1935	1333425	D&P	Cursor with springy metal fastener
1935	1348341	AW Faber	Cursor
1935	1354648	AW Faber	Darmstadt slide rule
1936	1362773	D&P	Slide rule made of polyvinyl plastic
1936	1363167	AW Faber	Slide rule, System Kramer
1936	1365908	D&P	Slide rule for reinforced concrete stressed up to 1500 kg
1936	1394384	AW Faber	Slide rule
1937	1400134	AW Faber	Slide rule for surveying
1937	1400877	D&P	Slide rule made from plastic (Acrylglas)
1937	1401260	D&P	A read-out window (index) for slide rules
1940	1482723	D&P	Slide rule made from plastic
1940	1483652	D&P	Slide rule made by laminating flat material
1940	1483653	D&P	Slide rule with transparent (Plexiglass) floors
1940	1483654	D&P	Stator made of several plastic components
1940	1484667	AW Faber	"Frameless" cursor
1940	1486119	AW Faber	Slide rule, Leipzig Trade Fair
1941	1506113	AW Faber	Slide rule
1942	1520081	D&P	Slide rule made of cardboard with scales that are flush (i.e., at the same elevation)

Appendix I

Slide Rule Patents (DRP and DBP) Related to Slide Rules

(Compiled with assistance from Günter Kugel. Patents since 1948 are limited to those issued by the Federal Government of Germany and do not include any issued by the East German Government.)

Year	Pat. No.	Maker or Applicant	Nation-ality	Claim briefly described	Actually Marketed
1878	756	FA Sheppard	USA	Slide rule with two slides.	No
1879	5860	G. Fuller	Ire.	Cylindrical slide rule(Eventually made byStanley of London).	Yes
1886	34583	D&P	G	Stable scale (celluloid laminated on wood).	Yes
1891	63051	K&E	USA	Duplex slide rule.	in USA
????	78611	Haedicke	G	Rules for the determination of the number of digits visible in the floor of the stator whenever the slide is positioned to the right or left.	No
1899	102589	JGD Mack	USA	One-sided slide rule with two-part stator connected by spiral springs and three alignment rods.	Yes
1901	126499	D&P	G	Spring-loaded stator for self-adjusting tension on side.	Yes
1902	132347	S. Masera	G	Slide rule with scales on an endless loop instead of a slide.	No
1903	158452	FJ Anderson	Ire.	Slide rule with segmented ("gridiron") scales, index arms on the ends of the slide, and a decimal-tracking System.	No
1905	163933	FJ Vaes	NL	Slide rule composed only of slides.	No
1905	173660	Nestler	G	Elastic celluloid panel connecting the two halves of the stator with resulting spring-loaded stator.	
1907	206428	Faber	G	Metal strips imbedded in the stator and slide perpendicular to the scales, to improve stability.	Yes
1907	207234	R. Nelting	G	Celestial navigation slide rule with two slides and adjustable cursor. Eventually made by D&P	Yes
1908	207530	W. Welsch	G	Slide rule with cylindrical slide.	No
1909	215722	Pickworth	G	Stator floor milled out for cubic scale. Eventually made by AW Faber.	Yes

1909	222297	F-C	G	Collapsible magnifying cursor with cut glass lens.	Yes
1909	225528	D&P	G	Cursor guide for one-sided slide rules.	Yes
1909	227582	D&P	G	Hard metal cursor with soft metal inserts to retain the lens.	Yes
1921	346209	D&P	G	Slide with gearing for vernier adjustment with two drive wheels or pinions.	Yes
1922	351899	H. Seehase	G	Technique for making metal slide rules with etched scales.	Yes
1922	364364	Reiss	G	"Phoenix Cursor," a form of "frameless cursor" that is "easy" to replace or repair and align.	
1922	365393	W. Lissauer	G	Slide rule with two springy slide guides connected with screws.	No
1922	365637	F-C	G	Stator parts connected by screws that permit adjustment of the slide action.	Yes
1923	373071	Bandermann	G	Slide rule with decimal position indicator in disk form on the end of the slide.	No
1924	388690	P Berville	F	Magnifying cursor for slide rules of various widths.	No
1924	394337	H Seehase	G	Tabular slide rule design with transparent plastic casing. Eventually produced by the Committee for Efficient Production.	Yes
1924	410565	Nestler	G	Stator halves connected by rings embedded in the well or floor of the stator.	Yes
1926	450304	F-C	G	An adjustable half-cylinder lens in the cursor frame.	Yes
1928	460655	F Netz	G	Metal slide rule with two independent cursors, one for two addition-subtraction scales and one for two multiplication-division scales.	
1928	499260	H Seehase	G	Expanded version of Patent #394337. Eventually produced by the Committee for Efficient Production.	Yes
1930	559664	F-C	G	Metal core (or bands) fastened in plastic with rivets or screws.	Yes
1932	574594	F-C	G	Duplex slide rule with adjustable strap-joint. (Plastic)	No
1933	596286	F-C	G	Duplex side rule with adjustable strap-joint.	No
1933	625535	F-C	G	Cursor for duplex slide rule.	No

1935	650658	Nestler	G	Cursor with window on the side.	Yes
1936	651442	Holzmeyer /Babel	G	Slide rule with compensation achieved by two-sided celluloid lamination.	No
1936	655353	C. Kübler	G	Slide rule with adding device (Addiator) on the back. Eventually produced by Faber-Castell.	Yes
1937	684135	F-C	G	Metal slide rule with plastic veneer.	No
1942	729162	H Seehase	G	Tabular slide composed of flat scales in a spring-loaded casing. Eventually produced by the Committee for Efficient Production.	Yes
1944	747007	H Seehase	G	Tabular slide rule. Extension of Patent #729162. Spring pressure perpendicular to the surface of the scales. Eventually produced by the Committee for Efficient Production.	Yes
1951	804932	M. Schirmer	G	Measuring and calculating device for the the graphic trades. Eventually produced by Faber-Castell (Model 2/66).	Yes
1951	805444	H Hehse	G	Logarithmic slide rule (for cross-sections of reinforced concrete).	Unk.
1951	812849	A Müller	G	Slide rule with decimal point tracking on stator, slide, and cursor.	No
1951	821840	F Kluge	G	Device for testing concrete. Made in the form of a slide rule. Eventually produced by Faber-Castell. (Model 2/62).	Yes
1951	824850	Hillebrand	G	Measuring stick and slide rule for reinforced concrete.	Unk.
1951	824854	B Bischoff	G	Slide rule made of sheet metal. Stator formed from one piece in which the slide is inserted.	Unk.
1951	873455	F-C/ Bachmann	G	Duplex slide rule strap-joint that are screwed on and adjustable.	Yes
1951	873456	F-C/ Bachmann	G	Cursor for duplex slide rule (adjustable).	Yes

1951	917215	Nestler	G	Plastic stator halves connected by ring-shaped springs. Extension of Patent #410565.	Yes
1952	1018659	F-C/ Bachmann	G	Slide rule with two cursors and diagram (Model 3/31 – for reinforced concrete)	Yes
1952	1062040	F-C/ Buelow	G	Window for Addiator inserted in floor of stator (plastic), riveted.	Yes
1952	1115967	F-C/ Tegtmeyer/ Bachmann	G	Cursor which attaches around a single-sided slide rule (Mathema)	Yes
1962	1128193	W Schönner	G	Slide rule for instructional and promotional purposes. (Electrically driven slide and cursor).	No
1962	1135686	F-C/ Bachmann	G	Slide rule with spring between slide and groove (to make slide operation smoother).	No
1964	1170170	F-C/ Tegtmeyer	G	Grooves on the flanges of the slide of plastic slide rules.	Yes

Appendix II

Slide Rules of Some German Makers

(The following lists of the most important models do not claim to be complete.)

Dennert & Pape Hamburg - Altona   ARISTO

Art. No.	Description	Material	Scale length cm
Models up to 1905 (in catalog order):			
338	Dennert & Pape I with cell facings	Boxwood	25
339	Dennert & Pape II "	Boxwood	50
340	Dennert & Pape III "	Boxwood	25
342	Simplex as 338 "	Boxwood	12.5
343	Simplex as 342 "	Mahogany	25
344	Simplex without cell facings	Boxwood	25
345	Simplex with metal cursor without glass	Boxwood	25
346	Exponential slide rule system, W. Schweth	Mahogany	25
347	Shipbuilding, Ing. Stockhusen	Mahogany	35
348	T-girder profiles	Mahogany	20
349	Tachymeter system, C. Werner	Mahogany	25
Models up to 1935:			
5	Normal without Trig.	Mahogany	25
5 ½	Normal with Trig.	Mahogany	25
6	Rietz without CI-scale, without Trig.	Mahogany	25
6 ½	Rietz without CI-scale, with Trig.	Mahogany	25
72	Normal with Trig.	Mahogany	15
2/28	Normal with Trig.	Mahogany	25
2/53	Normal with Trig.	Mahogany	50
19/15	Precision	Mahogany	12.5
19/28	Precision	Mahogany	25
19/53	Precision	Mahogany	50
55/30	DUFIX double sided type	Mahogany	25
79	Rietz	Mahogany	12.5
9/28	Rietz	Mahogany	25
9/53	Rietz	Mahogany	50

8/28	Rietz without reciprocal scale	Mahogany	25
8/28/3	Rietz with reciprocal scale	Mahogany	25
141	Electro	Mahogany	12.5
143	Electro	Mahogany	25
145	Electro	Mahogany	50
49/20	Electro-Rietz	Mahogany	25
15/28	Exponent	Mahogany	25
155	Exponent	Mahogany	50
813	Extended exponent (6 LL- scales)	Mahogany	25
43/15	Business system, Dr. Stender	Mahogany	12.5
43/28	Business system, Dr. Stender	Mahogany	25
43/53	Business system, Dr. Stender	Mahogany	50
10	School-business	Mahogany	25
64/28	Board practice, cargo and navigation	Mahogan	25
65	Insurance slide rule system, Kurth	Mahogany	25
23/53	Tachymeter system, Werner	Mahogany	25
44/28	Der Schweizer Topograph	Mahogany	25
47/28	Material testing system, Weißkopf	Mahogany	25
52/23	Machine time system, Kresta	Mahogany	20
48/28	Universal surveyor and topography	Mahogany	30
48/53	Universal Landmesser Topographie	Mahogany	50
38/28	Steel concrete system, Dr. Ing. Lewe	Mahogany	30
60/32	Pipes system, Behrens	Mahogany	30
62/32	Colorator transm.o. heath a. cold syst. Behrens	Mahogany	30
18/28	Sewerage system, Vikari	Mahogany	30
72	Simzet (Normal with Trig.)	Mahogany	12.5
072	Simzet without Trig.	Mahogany	12.5
79	Riezet with Trig. and K, CI, L	Mahogany	12.5
079	Riezet without Trig.	Mahogany	12.5
12	Simplex with Trig.	Mahogany	12.5
012	Simplex without Trig.	Mahogany	12.5
12c	Simplex with Trig. with cell. Cursor	Mahogany	12.5
012c	Simplex without Trig. With cell. Cursor	Mahogany	12.5
12b	Kubus	Mahogany	12.5
012b	Kubus	Mahogany	12.5
120	Normal with Trig.	Mahogany	12.5
121	Normal withoutTrig.	Mahogany	12.5
14/15	Business	Mahogany	12.5
30	Elfit with Trig.	Mahogany	12.5
31	Elfit without Trig.	Celluloid	12.5

and series C:

C 16	Shipbuilding system Stockhusen	Mahogany	25
C 17	Slide rule for weights	Mahogany	25
C 18	Sewerage	Mahogany	25
C 20	Direct lighting	Mahogany	25
C 22	Land-registry controller	Mahogany	25
C 34	Four-digits slide rule	Mahogany	25
C 36	Telefunken	Mahogany	25
C 40	Turbine slide rule	Mahogany	25
C 45	Condensation slide rule	Mahogany	5
C 46	Chemists slide rule	Mahogany	25

Further models:

Z 28	Azimuth	Mahogany	25
229	Nautical astronomy	Mahogany	25
230	Celestial altitude azimuth	Mahogany	25
19/15	Präzision w. folded scale	Mahogany	12.5
19/28	Präzision w. folded scale	Mahogany	25
19/53	Präzision w. folded scale	Mahogany	50

Condensed (War) program 1939 up to 1945 (WW II):

92	Normal	Plastic	25
99	Rietz	Plastic	25
914	Electro	Plastic	25
943	Business	Plastic	25
967	Darmstadt	Plastic	25
95	Students	Plastic	25
96	Students	Plastic	25
910	Business	Plastic	25
945	Praktiker	Plastic	25
845	Commerz I	Plastic	12.5

Program from 1945 appr. to 1975:

89	Rietz	Plastic	12.5
99	Rietz	Plastic	25
109	Rietz	Plastic	50
89 400^g	Rietz	Plastic	12.5
99 400^g	Rietz 400^g	Plastic	25
109 400^g	Rietz 400^g	Plastic	50
803	Mono-Rietz	Plastic	12.5

810	Puck	Plastic	10
829	Multitrig	Plastic	12.5
867	Darmstadt	Plastic	12.5
868	Studio	Plastic	12.5
869	Studiolog	Plastic	12.5
870	Multilog	Plastic	12.5
0901	Junior	Plastic	25
0902	JuniorTrig	Plastic	25
0903	Scholar	Plastic	25
0903 LL	Scholar LL	Plastic	25
0903 VS2	Scholar VS 2	Plastic	25
0906	Bischolar	Plastic	25
0906 LL	Bischolar LL	Plastic	25
0907	Commerz Junior	Plastic	25
0908	Trilog	Plastic	25
0929	Multitrig	Plastic	25
623	Commerz III	Plastic	25
939	System Göttsch steel concrete n = 10	Plastic	25
965	Commerz II	Plastic	25
967	Darmstadt	Plastic	25
0968	Studio	Plastic	25
0969	Studiolog	Plastic	25
0970	Multilog	Plastic	25
0972	Hyperlog	Plastic	25
1067	Darmstadt	Plastic	50
01068	Studio	Plastic	50
01070	Multilog	Plastic	50
867 400^g	Darmstadt 400^g	Plastic	12.5
0968 400^g	Studio 400^g	Plastic	25

A.W. Faber until approximately1905; then A.W. Faber-Castell

Art. No.	Description	Material	Scale length cm

From catalog 1913 and before

* *all models in catalog 1931 order*

Art. No.	Description	Material	Scale length cm
307	Columbus system Rohrberg	Pearwood	25
308	Mittelschule A/B, C/D, with S, T	Beechwood	12.5
309	Mittelschule A/B, C/D with S, T	Pearwood	25
313S	Normal /(Mannheim)	Pearwood	12.5
314	Columbus	Pearwood	25
317	School-slide rule A/B, C/D with S, T	Maplewood	25
319	Electro w. recipr.a. cube scale	Pearwood	12.5
326	Normal A/B, C/D	Pearwood	15
332	Mittelschule	Pearwood	12.5
338S	Normal-Trig. (Mannheim)	Pearwood	12.5
339	Mittelschule	Pearwood	25
340	Forester	Pearwood	25
341	Timber trade	Pearwood	25
342	"Columbus" syst. Rohrberg(sometimes ebony)	Pearwood	50
345	Barometric height difference (Dr. Hohenner)	Pearwood	25
347	Weight of iron girders syst.Schweppe-Äbli	Pearwood	25
348	Machine time system Dr. Winkel	Pearwood	25
349	Barometric height difference (Dr. Hohenner)	Pearwood	12.5
350	A.W. Faber (Mannheim), adj. Cursor	Boxwood	25
355	School slide rule	Maplewood	25
356	School slide rule	Maplewood	12.5
358	Cultivator of cereal grains	Boxwood	25
359	School slide rule	Maplewood	25
360	A.W. Faber-Slide rule (Mannheim)	Boxwood	25
360	Normal A/B, C/D	Pearwood	25
361	A.W. Faber-Slide rule (A/B, C/D)	Boxwood	25
363	A.W. Faber-Slide rule, as 360, w. add. Grad.	Boxwood	25
363	Normal with additional graduation	Pearwood	25
366	System Schumacher with number theor.indices	Boxwood	25
367	A.W. Faber with digit registering cursor	Boxwood	25
369	Normal pocket size, as 360	Pearwood	12.5
370	A.W. Faber, as 360	Boxwood	50
371	Steel concrete system Torda	Pearwood	25

374	System Pickworth	Boxwood	25
375	Rietz	Pearwood	25
377	System Pickworth, with digit regist. Cursor	Boxwood	25
378	Electro	Pearwood	25
379	Pocket size as 378	Boxwood	12.5
379	Electro	Pearwood	12.5
380	A.W. Faber, as 360	Boxwood	50
380N	Normal	Pearwood	50
382	Mannheim with 2 add. LL scales	Pearwood	50
384	System Pickworth	Boxwood	50
385N	Rietz with add. reciprocal scale	Pearwood	50
386	Rietz	Pearwood	12.5
387	Rietz with add. reciprocal scale	Pearwood	25
388N	Electro with recipr. and cube scale	Pearwood	50
389	Normal	Pearwood	10
392	Mannheim with 2 add. LL scales	Pearwood	25
394	Rietz	Pearwood	25
397S	Rietz	Pearwood	12.5
397	Rietz with add. reciprocal scale	Pearwood	12.5
398	Electro with recipr.a. cube scale	Pearwood	25

From the middle of the 1930s (except for **) to 1975 appr.

1/22	Disponent	Pearwood	25
1/22A **	Disponent with Addiator	Pearwood	25
1/27 **	Merchant-engineer	Pearwood	25
1/28	Bivius	Pearwood	25
1/33 **	System Kotteck expended sizes by roll on	Pearwood	25
1/38	Tachymeter	Pearwood	25
1/38 400^g	Tachymeter with grade	Pearwood	25
1/40 **	Forester	Pearwood	25
1/41 **	Timber trade	Pearwood	25
1/44	Ekagnost (electro-cardiography)	Pearwood	25
1/48	System Dr. Winkel machine time	Pearwood	25
1/52	Physicists	Pearwood	25
1/54	System Darmstadt	Pearwood	25
1/54A **	System Darmstadt with Addiator	Pearwood	25
1/60	Normal-Trig.	Pearwood	25
1/61 **	Normal	Pearwood	25
1/63 **	Normal-Trig with add. Numbers	Pearwood	25
1/64 **	Normal, add. artillery calcul.	Pearwood	25

1/70 **	System Rietz, add.artillery calcul.	Pearwood	25
1/71 **	System Torda (steel concrete)	Pearwood	25
1/75 **	System Rietz	Pearwood	25
1/78 **	Electro	Pearwood	25
1/87	System Rietz	Pearwood	25
1/87A **	System Rietz with Addiator	Pearwood	25
1/91 **	Industrial school	Pearwood	25
1/92	Exp. Modell log-log	Pearwood	25
1/94 **	System Rietz (add. name Kiel)	Pearwood	25
1/98	Electro	Pearwood	25
3/11	Steel concrete	Pearwood	30
3/42 **	Columbus system Rohrberg	Pearwood	35
4/60	Normal	Pearwood	50
4/87	Rietz	Pearwood	50
4/92	Log-Log	Pearwood	50
4/98	Electro	Pearwood	50
51/22 **	School-business	Beechwood	25
51/91 **	School A/B, C/D	Beechwood	25
51/94 **	Industrial school	Beechwood	25
63/22 **	Disponent (Celluloid with Pearwood inlet)	C.w. Pearwood	12.5
63/39 **	Normal	C.w. Pearwood	12.5
63/87 **	Rietz	C.w. Pearwood	12.5
63/91 **	Normal-Trig	C.w. Pearwood	12.5
63/22R**	Disponent with Addiator	C.w. Pearwood	12.5
63/39R**	Normal with Addiator	C.w. Pearwood	12.5
63/87R**	Rietz with Addiator	C.w. Pearwood	12.5
63/91R**	Normal-Trig. with Addiator	C.w. Pearwood	12.5
63/98R**	Electro with Addiator	C.w. Pearwood	12.5

From 1945

2/31	Duplex type steel concrete	Plastic	25
2/62	Dywidag system Kluge cement mixture	Plastic	25
2/66	Demegraph system Schirmer	Plastic	25
2/82	Duplex type DUPLEX	Plastic	25
2/82N	Duplex type DUPLEX , extended version	Plastic	25
2/83	Duplex type NOVO-DUPLEX	Plastic	25
2/83N	Duplex type NOVO-DUPLEX ext. Version	Plastic	25
2/84	Mathema	Plastic	25
2/84N	Mathema duplex type, new version	Plastic	25
3/31	Steel concrete, 2 cursors	Pearwood	30

4/22	Disponent	Pearwood	50
4/38 360°	Tachymeter	Pearwood	50
4/38 400^g	Tachymeter	Pearwood	50
4/54	Darmstadt	Pearwood	50
4/54 400^g	Darmstadt	Pearwood	50
12/82	Duplex type DUPLEX (export version)	Plastic	25
52/80	Mentor beginners duplex type	Plastic	25
52/81	Novo-Mentor duplex type	Plastic	25
52/82	Schul-D-Stab duplex type	Plastic	25
57/22	Students business	Plastic	25
57/62	Dywidag system Kluge (substitut. 2/62)	Plastic	25
57/74	Textil-slide rule system Schirdewan	Plastic	25
57/86	Columbus A/B, C/D	Plastic	25
57/87	Schul-Rietz	Plastic	25
57/88	Schul-Rietz N (Advanced Rietz)	Plastic	25
57/89	Students-Super-Log-Log	Plastic	25
57/92	Students log-log	Plastic	25
62/82	Duplex pocket size	Plastic	12.5
62/82N	Duplex neu pocket size	Plastic	12.5
62/83	Novo-Duplex pocket size	Plastic	12.5
62/83N	Novo-Duplex ext. vers. pocket size	Plastic	12.5
63/39	Normal (exp.version)	Plastic	12.5
63/82	Duplex (Exp.Vers.)	Plastic	12.5
63/83	Novo-Duplex (exp.version)	Plastic	12.5
63/87	Rietz (exp. Version)	Plastic	12.5
63/91	Normal-Trig (exp.vers.)	Plastic	12.5
67/21	Steel concrete pocket size	Plastic	12.5
67/22	Business pocket size	Plastic	12.5
67/22 R	Business pocket size with Addiator	Plastic	12.5
67/32	Paper and cardboards system Kramer	Plastic	12.5
67/34	Hämognost (content of haemoglobin)	Plastic	12.5
67/38	Tachymeter pocket size	Plastic	12.5
67/39	Normal A/B, C/D	Plastic	12.5
67/54	Darmstadt pocket size double edge	Plastic	12.5
67/54b	Darmstadt pocket size one edge	Plastic	12.5
67/54 R	Darmstadt pocket size w. Addiator double edge	Plastic	12.5
67/54Rb	Darmstadt pocket size w. Addiator one edge	Plastic	12.5
67/56	Welding engineering system, Titscher	Plastic	12.5
67/87	Rietz pocket size	Plastic	12.5
67/87 R	Rietz pocket size with Addiator	Plastic	12.5

67/91	Normal-Trig	Plastic	12.5
67/98	Electro pocket size double edge	Plastic	12.5
67/98b	Electro pocket size one edge	Plastic	12.5
67/98Rb	Electro pocket size one edge w. Add.	Plastic	12.5
67/98 R	Electro pocket size double edge w. Addiator	Plastic	12.5
111/22	Business	Plastic	25
111/22A	Business	Plastic	25
111/38	Tachymeter	Plastic	25
111/48	Machine time syst.Dr. Winkel (distr.1/48)	Plastic	25
111/54	Darmstadt	Plastic	25
111/54 A	Darmstadt w. Addiator	Plastic	25
111/66	Demegraph system Schirmer (distr.2/66)	Plastic	25
111/87	Rietz	Plastic	25
111/87 A	Rietz w. Addiator	Plastic	25
111/98	Electro	Plastic	25
152/81	Novo-Mentor (exp.version)	Plastic	25
152/82	DUPLO (exp. Version)	Plastic	25
157/80	Mentor-Fix	Plastic	25
157/87	Schul-Rietz (Exp.version)	Plastic	25
163/81	Novo-Mentor (Exp.version)	Plastic	12.5
167/87	Rietz	Plastic	12.5
167/87g	Rietz (Exp.version)	Plastic	12.5
180/082	Schul-D-Stab Joh. Faber (Exp.version)	Plastic	25

Demonstration slide rules and projection slide rules are not included although they constituted another 30 variants. Also, there are Models 57/87, 57/88, and 57/89 which were made in Grabs (Canton St. Gallen) and were marked "Made in Switzerland". Model 52/82 marked "Made in Austria" was made in the A.W. Faber-Castell factory in Engelhartzell, Upper Austria.

In the case of early Faber models, the trade-mark was usually printed on the stator in the well under the slide. The trademark also appeared in gold or in black on the front of the stator. In addition, the letters CASTELL appeared on most models on the front of the slide. In most cases the date of manufacture was stamped on the back of the stator, for example "3" on the left indicated March and "54" on the right indicated 1954. Sometimes the date would be stamped as three or four numbers, e.g., 764 meant July 1964.

Albert Nestler   **NESTLER**

Art. No.	Description	Material	Scale length cm
From catalog 1911/12 and before			
1	Industrial school, A/B, C/D, pocket size	Mahogany	12.5
1a	Industrial school, A/B, C/D	Mahogany	25
2	Industrial school, without cursor(!)	Mahogany	20
3	Industrial school, without cursor(!)	Mahogany	25
4	Slide rule	Mahogany	20
5	Slide rule	Mahogany	25
6	Slide rule, pocket size	Ivory	12.5
7	Slide rule	Ivory	20
8	Slide rule	Ivory	25
9	Slide rule	German silver	25
9a	Spanischer Tacheometer, without cursor	German silver	40
10	Slide rule	Mahogany	25
10a	Slide rule	Mahogany	25
11	Slide rule, pocket size	Mahogany	12.5
12	Slide rule, pocket size	Mahogany	12.5
12/5	Slide rule, rough scale	Mahogany	25
12a	Slide rule, pocket size	Mahogany	12.5
12c	Slide rule	Mahogany	15
12b	Slide rule, with magnifier	Mahogany	12.5
12d	Slide rule, with magnifier	Mahogany	15
13	Slide rule	Mahogany	20
14	Slide rule	Mahogany	25
17	Slide rule	Mahogany	35
18	Slide rule	Mahogany	50
19	Slide rule	Mahogany	60
19a	Slide rule	Mahogany	100
13L	Slide rule w. semicyl. Magnifier	Mahogany	20
14L	Slide rule w. semicyl. Magnifier	Mahogany	25
17L	Slide rule w. semicyl. Magnifier	Mahogany	35
18L	Slide rule w. semicyl. Magnifier	Mahogany	50
22	Slide rule system Rietz	Mahogany	15
23	Slide rule system Rietz	Mahogany	25
23a	Slide rule system Rietz	Mahogany	35
24	Slide rule system Rietz	Mahogany	50

24a	Slide rule system Rietz	Mahogany	60
24b	Slide rule system Rietz	Mahogany	100
22L	Slide rule system Rietz w. semicyl. Magnifier	Mahogany	15
23L	Slide rule system Rietz w. semicyl. Magnifier	Mahogany	25
23aL	Slide rule system Rietz w. semicyl. Magnifier	Mahogany	36
24L	Slide rule system Rietz m. semicyl. Magnifier	Mahogany	50
25	Slide rule system Perry	Mahogany	25
26	Slide rule system Tscherepaschinski	Mahogany	25
26a	Slide rule system Tscherepaschinski	Mahogany	50
27	Slide rule Präzision	Mahogany	25
27a	Slide rule Präzision	Mahogany	50
28	Slide rule Universal	Mahogany	25
28a	Slide rule Universal	Mahogany	50
29	Duplex type slide rule	Mahogany	25
30	Slide rule system Nestle	Mahogany	25
31	Slide rule timber business	Mahogany	20
32	Slide rule Electro	Mahogany	25
33	Slide rule Chemiker	Mahogany	25
34	Slide rule system Hanauer	Mahogany	25
35	Slide rule system Peter	Mahogany	25
36	Slide rule f. weaving and spinning mills	Mahogany	36
37	Slide rule Electro	Mahogany	25
38	Slide rule Perfekt	Mahogany	25

Additional models in the 1930s

13L, 14/1, 14/3, 18/3, 23/1, 23/3, 23R/3, 23aR/1, 24R/3, 24R/1, 22E, 23E,

L = additional magnifier
/1 = cursor with one hairline
/3 = cursor with three hairlines
R = with reciprocal scale
E = Ivory-imitation

39	Electro, system Besser	Mahogany	25
40/15	Kaufmann	Mahogany	15
40/25	Kaufmann	Mahogany	25
40a/50	Kaufmann	Mahogany	50
41	Liliput, with S u. T	Mahogany	10
42	Liliput, without S u. T	Mahogany	10
43	Steel concrete, system Nestler-Hoffmann	Mahogany	25

New program 1945 - ca. 1973

0115	Techniker	Plastic	12.5
0123	Rietz	Plastic	12.5
0121	Darmstadt	Plastic	12.5
0129	Polymath-Duplex	Plastic	12.5
0137	Electro	Plastic	12.5
0149	Steel concrete system Maarschalk	Plastic	12.5
and 7 demonstration-slide rules			
0127	International	Plastic	12.5
0140	Kaufmann	Plastic	12.5
0210	Darmstadt	Mahogany	25
0215	Darmstadt	Mahogany	50
0232	Rietz	Mahogany	25
0235	Rietz	Mahogany	50
0239	Schul-Rietz	Plastic	25
0251	Alpha	Plastic	25
0252	Beta (duplex type)	Plastic	25
0253	Gamma (duplex-type)	Plastic	25
0254	Delta (duplex type)	Plastic	25
0260	Mecanica (machine time)	Mahogany	25
0275	Präzision	Mahogany	50
0281	Geometer	Mahogany	25
0289	Rietz-Duplex (duplex-type)	Plastic	25
0291	Polymath-Duplex (duplex type)	Plastic	25
0292	Multimath-Duplex (duplex type)	Plastic	25
0297	Electronic	Plastic	25
0330	Chemiker	Plastic	25
0370	Electro	Mahogany	25
0401	Merkur	Plastic	25
0409	Schul-Merkur	Plastic	25
0440	Steel concrete system Maarschalk	Plastic	25

REISS

Art. No.	Description	Material	Scale length cm
2812	Pocket size Simplex A,B,C,D,S,T	Mahogany	12.5
2813	Normal Simplex	Mahogany	25
2814	Demonstration slide rule	Pearwood	200
2815	Slide rule Dr. Frank, extended scale	Mahogany	25
1041	Slide rule	Mahogany	25
1042	Slide rule	Mahogany	50
1044	Slide rule with springy lamin. floor	Mahogany	25
1147	Slide rule for timber business	Pearwood	25
1141	Stellfix T	Mahogany	25
1143	Stellfix K	Mahogany	25
1145	Surveyor Py-Lo system Seifert	Mahogany	30
2812 ½	Pocket size	Pearwood	12.5
2813	Pocket size Rietz	Pearwood	12.5
2813R	Pocket size Rietz w. recipr.scale	Pearwood	12.5
1041½ L	Slide rule	Pearwood	25
3250½L	Slide rule w. adjusting screws	Pearwood	25
3251½L	Slide rule	Pearwood	50
5128½IIIP	Slide rule Rietz	Mahogany	25
5128½ III	Slide rule Rietz	Mahogany	25
5128 III	Slide rule Rietz w. adjusting screws	Mahogany	25
5129 III	Slide rule Rietz w. adjusting screws	Mahogany	50
5128/15	Pocket size Rietz	Mahogany	12.5
3256 P III	Slide rule Electro	Mahogany	25
3789 ½	Slide rule "Präzision"	Mahogany	25

Following models from 1945

3203	Slide rule Rietz	Metal	25
3204	Slide rule Darmstadt	Metal	25
3223	Duplex type Slide rule Progress	Metal	25
3214	Slide rule Disponent	Plastic	25
3214	Slide rule Darmstadt record	Plastic	25
3236	Slide rule Darmstadt	Plastic	25
3212	Slide rule Darmstadt- Rietz	Plastic	25

Index

Index

Index